Earth Foods

Earth Foods

By
Lee Fryer
and
Dick Simmons

Follett
Publishing
Company,
Chicago

Grateful acknowledgment is made to the following for use of
   material reprinted herein:

From *An Agricultural Testament* by Sir Albert Howard.
   Reprinted by permission of Oxford University Press.

From *Food Farming and the Future* by Friend Sykes.
   Reprinted by permission of Faber and Faber Ltd.

From "Variation in Mineral Composition of Vegetables" from
   Proceedings of the Soil Science Society of America, Volume
   13, 1948.
   Reprinted by permission of the
   Soil Science Society of America.

From the *Cleveland Plain Dealer* article by John Beaber of
   July 21, 1963 which was incorporated into
   the hearings on Federal Pesticide Control Act
   of 1971 (House). Reprinted by permission
   of the *Cleveland Plain Dealer*.

From *A World of Breads* by Delores Casella.
   Copyright © 1966 by Delores Casella.
   Reprinted by permission of David White Company.

From the article "Millions of Chickens Tainted" in the
   July 29, 1971 issue of the *Washington Post*.
   Reprinted by permission of the
   Washington Post.

Library of Congress Catalogue Card Number: 77-183077

ISBN: 0-695-80311-5

First printing

FOREWORD 🐦

THERE IS an oft-quoted phrase that comes to mind upon reading *Earth Foods*:

> "The fact is there is only one major disease—and that is malnutrition."

This pronouncement was made by Dr. C. W. Cavanaugh, of Cornell University, some years ago.

Many noted doctors, such as Drs. Emanuel Cheraskin and W. M. Ringsdorf, Jr., of the University of Alabama, have recently corroborated Dr. Cavanaugh's statement. "Nutrition is a big problem today," Dr. Cheraskin said. "There are many diseases that are rampant in the United States and groceries have something to do with it."

Foods can be broken down into two categories—resistance agents, which tend to help the body fight off disease, and susceptibility agents. Doctors say if you look at the diets of sick people and healthy people, they are different. If you give sick people the diet of healthy people, they don't stay sick so long.

Dr. Roger Williams, of the University of Texas, after years of research, "believes that a diet that provides body cells all the nutrients they need to function properly can help prevent mental retardation, mental illness, arthritis, heart disease—and even cancer." (National Observer, 2 November 6, 1971.)

The lack of certain minerals, vitamins, enzymes or sufficient protein in our diet (a lack of ex Vita B_6, for instance, is seemingly related to schizophrenia) seems to disturb our natural chemical balance, lessen our ability to develop antibodies against viruses, and weaken our immune mechanisms.

As the food comes off the farm, it already lacks many of the necessary nutrients for health as a result of the poisoned, poorly nourished, over-exploited and depleted soil.

The food is then taken over by the food processor, who deliberately kills most of the remaining nutritive elements so that it will not spoil in transit or on the grocer's shelf. The processor adds a host of highly questionable chemicals, such as preservatives, flavorings, antibiotics, moisturizers, dryers, solvents, colorings, bleaches, fillers, and cosmetics, until there is very little nourishment left. Even the affluent end up malnourished and fair prey to any virus or germ that comes along.

This general idea runs like a subliminal impulse through the pages of this important book.

Anyone who reads and stays awake these days is smart enough to know that the farm complex of the United States no longer produces nutritious, contamination-free food. Hidden hunger and slow deterioration of the population is being accomplished in the name of technology, efficiency, super-enterprise and high progress.

Why? Because a fiction is being kept alive that the farm plant cannot produce enough food to feed the people unless toxic chemicals that may be genetically unsafe rain like a tropical squall across the nation's cropland acres.

The plain truth is that chemical farming is obsolete, and the production of substandard foods is inexcusable.

America wants safe, certified food. People are willing to pay for quality, but they insist on getting what they pay for. When they buy a carrot or a tomato, they want a pure carrot or tomato, not synthetic, poisoned pulp that looks like the real article.

But *Earth Foods* is more than a plea for groceries with substance and balance. Lee Fryer and Dick Simmons have brought us news of the most vital importance. It is the kind of stuff we sometimes call exposé—with one difference! Exposé is almost always negative. Yet here we have exposé that details the problem and follows with a solution. Application of the principles unveiled in *Earth Foods* will allow America to develop an ecologically sound farm technology, a more intelligent approach to food processing, a plan for true preventive medicine and a hope for a healthier, happier, growing America.

Eddie Albert
Pacific Palisades,
California

CONTENTS ✒

Earth Foods

Our Food
Revolution

EARTH FOODS is a book about America's food problems. If
you, as a consumer, suspect that you may not be getting
your money's worth when you load your shopping cart
once a week, you're probably right.

This book will explain how food today has been debased: it has been both poisoned and robbed of its natural
nutritional stockpile. On the one hand, you may not be
getting all that you think you are, and on the other hand,
you may be getting things you are not even aware of. The
biggest, most picture-perfect orange on the grocery store
shelf does not automatically give you more nutrition, more
vitamin C and minerals, than a puny orange with brown
spots. That luscious, juicy red steak or that plump, cheerful chicken may very possibly contain hidden poison from
harmful growth stimulants pumped into them when they
were still walking around.

This book has many revelations important to you. City
dwellers may be surprised to discover that enormous piles
of wastes produced by huge confined colonies of chickens
or cattle and streams of untreated blood pouring out of
slaughterhouses present problems as real and terrible for
the environment as the automobiles or industry they already know about. Yet by re-cycling the wastes, not with

old-fashioned or "organic" composting, but by modern methods of processing them and then using them as fertilizers, the quality of the food we eat can be radically improved, along with the condition of the environment.

Earth Foods is a positive book, not just a negative, critical one. It challenges the rigid, unhelpful ideas of your food suppliers and storekeepers and asks them to respond instead to organized efforts by consumers to get what they want and need from the U.S. business system. One of the main objectives of this book is to help you to act effectively by arming you with good information and sound ideas.

You know already that you don't want mercury in your tuna or stilbestrol, the female hormone, in your beef. You don't want billowy empty loaves of tasteless white bread, however many ways they're supposed to build strong bodies. Neither do you want to pay 50¢ a head for "organic" lettuce and 75¢ a loaf for "organic" bread. What should you demand?

U.S. agriculture as a whole will not be de-mechanized, de-chemicalized or returned to individual small farms— nor should it be, necessarily. The food industry will not cease to process, pack and put preservatives into foods so they can endure the long trip into the urban markets, and we will have to live with this.

But there is a possibility of what we will call a "Certified Earth Food." This is a new kind of food concept, which presents a sane middle ground, something between the billowy loaves of white bread and the hopelessly expensive "organic" foods. Some Earth Foods, specially grown to high but realistic ecological and nutritional standards, are already available at reasonable prices in a few supermarkets, and they are an important trend in the consumer's food battle. More and more food producers can give us this kind of merchandise, and can do so while still maintaining their own profits.

As they are presently available, the "Certified Earth Foods" label tells you at least three things:

1) You are sure of the nutrition you are getting: your food has been independently tested to insure that at least the minimal level of the vitamins and minerals you expect are in it.

2) You know that it is free of things that might harm you: in its growth, it was not drowned in harmful fertilizers or pesticides, nor was it injected with questionable hormones and growth stimulants.

3) You are also certain that it is safe for the environment: our pollution problems were not increased by its growth and production—fruit, animal or vegetable, its wastes have been processed and cycled back into the environment.

Let's backtrack, though: how and why, exactly, is our food getting debased? Is it an accident, or is someone doing this deliberately, and when and why did it all begin?

First of all, once we had a workable good food system. Prior to World War II, the U.S. food supply system was basically sound. For one thing, fertilizing of crops was moderate. An excessive and unbalanced use of nitrogen to get high yields of crops had not begun then. Farm and garden chemicals were bio-degradable and did not have insidious long-term effects. The common pesticides with chlorinated hydro-carbons and phenoxy combinations such as DDT, aldrin, endrin 2 or 4-5T, were not in use.

For another thing, animals and poultry were raised on reasonably balanced diets: they were not force-fed, or given growth stimulants. They were not kept in forced confinement, so that they could not burn up calories or lose weight by running around. They were not pumped full of antibiotics and pharmaceuticals, so that none, not even the sickliest animals, would die. A process of natural selection took place in those days, and only the finest, healthiest animals reached our tables.

Lastly, foods were being processed and prepared for sale with a moderate use of additives, extenders, preservatives, cosmetics and sweeteners then. The massive additions of questionable materials so common today were not standard practice then.

What happened to change all those sensible, moderate farming practices? For one thing, the technical advances of World War II served to industrialize U.S. agriculture. The new chemicals born during the war were adapted for insect, disease and weed controls, and the new high-power machines were put to use in the cultivation and harvesting of crops. These innovations in turn eliminated the need for millions of sharecroppers, small farmers and farm workers, and reduced rural employment opportunities to nothing. With no economic base, twenty million rural people migrated to the cities over the next two decades, where they swelled the downtowns and exploded the suburbs.

This process is called urbanization, and apart from destroying the lives of millions of rural people, it had profound harmful effects on the food supply system. It concentrates the areas where food is consumed, and isolates them at great distances from the areas where the food is actually produced. It creates a huge demand for uniform quantities and kinds of foods: thousands of people have the same needs for meat, milk, eggs, fruit, vegetables, etc. Such a market situation is the perfect business environment for supermarkets, and then super-supermarkets, which can receive and dispense the products of giant farms, feedlots and automated food industries.

The debasing of our foods, then, was simply the logical result as food was commercially adapted to fit this mass food production and distribution system. Fresh fruits, vegetables, eggs, milk and chickens? No longer possible. Grow them in California, Mexico, Florida, Arkansas or Wisconsin. Freeze, pack, can sterilize, neutralize, devitalize and treat them, then ship them to market. Natural sausages, meats, cereals, or baked goods? Ridiculous. Embalm the meats and bake the breads in ovens three blocks long. No one will know the difference in the cities, anyway. Boil the milk so it will keep longer and add coal tar to cover the funny taste. Put sawdust in the hamburger so it won't shrink. The people who are doing this are not part of some terrible conspiracy. They honestly have forgotten that making things bigger is not the only goal.

Why are consumers so concerned now, if the food producers are not? Well, there has been information available in the United States for the past 30 years, but all of us became really concerned and better and better informed with the publication of *Silent Spring* in 1962, which began the awakening in most of our minds. Since then the books and magazines of the famous although recently deceased J. I. Rodale on organic foods and how important they can be to us all have added to the impact on a thoughtful and concerned community. *Organic Gardening* was started in 1942, and *Prevention* has been with us since 1950. By 1965, their combined circulation was 750,000, and by 1971, it had grown to 1,700,000—a wide audience of alarmed Americans, indeed.

In the kitchens of America as well as in the supermarkets, there has been a revolution taking place. Adelle Davis

5

has published two excellent books on food, *Let's Eat Right to Keep Fit* and *Let's Cook It Right*, and at least three million homemakers have paid enough attention to want her words on their bookshelves. Catharyn Elwood, another venerable woman with good sense about food, has written *Feel like a Million*, in which she pitilessly assesses our mounting food and water supply problems. These two women by themselves, although they are not the only authors with sensible suggestions about our food, have brought food science out of the college cloisters of home economics courses and the musty Department of Agriculture laboratory reports and into the consciousness of today's food buyers. We all eat, and there is no reason why we cannot all know what makes good food for us, and what does not.

Another aspect of the problem has been attacked by the magazine, *Consumer Reports*, which has done a praiseworthy job of informing the public about what to look for in the labelling of foods, and how to evaluate the sometimes deceptive labels. Although of course the magazine does not deal only with food, it has been so useful a tool to millions of Americans that its circulation has also skyrocketed: in 1940, it reached 78,000 homes, and by 1971, two million homes read it regularly.

Ralph Nader, generally known for exposing the errors of the Detroit auto magnates, presented a damning report to the Senate Select Committee on Foods and Human Needs in 1969, and the food industry, too, stood on shakier ground in the minds of Americans. Because his work on that report was so carefully documented, however, and because his suggestions for upgrading the food we all consume did have merit, now even many private food industry people consider his work constructive.

When the news of the discovery of the mercury contained in swordfish and tuna reached the papers, it seemed that it was the last straw to the American food buying public. Actually, though, it was a scandal whose news should be considered minor, since the harm done was actually minor compared to the harm done by other poisons in our foods. The uproar was sufficient, however, to dramatize once and for all that poison was in our foods. The question was suddenly overwhelming: "What else is in my dinner?"

What do all these newly awakened food consumers, the new revolutionaries, look like now, then? Let's create two likely vignettes:

First we have a third stage feminine food revolutionary. She is basically sweet and moderate, but she has read most of the books and magazines listed above, and she is carrying a copy of *Consumer Reports* in her handbag. She is very concerned.

She goes to the vegetable section of the supermarket and pokes the big insincere heads of lettuce. "All nitrogen, no vitamins," she says and passes on. She tastes a sprig of celery. It is not sweet and is flat. "No minerals," she says, and passes by. She snickers at the sickly tomatoes, caged in their cello paks. "Poor things," she says, and passes on to the gorgeous looking apples and peaches. "Mustn't taste, might poison," she says, and passes on.

The tuna and other canned fish are just ahead. She detours a whole aisle to avoid thinking of mercury, and goes past the TV dinners and instant waffles to the poultry, at 31¢ a pound. "Ugh," she says, "it'll have blue bones and taste like cellophane because they grew it too fast." The meat is next. She has just read Rodale's article in *Prevention* about feeding beef stil-

7

bestrol, the synthetic female hormone, which makes it grow and fatten faster. Over 80% of all U.S. beef are fed this dubious stuff, according to Rodale, and it can cause cancer and genetic disturbances. It also tends to make the meat soft and tasteless.

Our lady leaves the meat hurriedly, passes though the bread section, where the billowy empty loaves that build fine bodies 11 ways crowd the shelves. Did she buy anything? Yes, she bought a gallon of pure spring water for 89¢, remembering that Catharyn Elwood said recently in one of her lectures, "I wouldn't feed U.S. city water to a rat!"

Here now is a successful business man. He pays attention to the evidence and makes decisions carefully. He has been reading the news stories and magazine articles about food quality and environmental matters. Finally, he says, "I've got to change. They are raising hell with our foods. They don't taste like they used to, and this DDT is bad."

So, being a direct action man, he goes shopping at the nearby health food store. He goes in, feeling a bit silly and sinful. The lady proprietor, chewing on an organic carrot, says, "Did you know you've been eating wrong or you wouldn't have all that grey hair?" He says, "What shall I do about it?" She says, "Eat organic carrots and raw gland tissue tablets."

Privately, he doesn't believe the grey hair business. Grey hair is in his family, through his grandfather and all his brothers. He goes on to the food counters. The apples are puny and boast a few worm holes. This shows that they are organic. The potatoes are 30¢ a pound. Carrots are 40¢ a pound and lettuce is

50¢ a head. "Flew it all in from California," the lady proudly says. The bread is 75¢ a loaf.

Our man prowls through the maze of vitamins and food supplements that look like a 1915 apothecary store, past the dried dandelions and the cucumber soap. He buys a sesame candy bar and thoughtfully goes his way.

If the vignettes seem silly, they do illustrate the question, what can a concerned person eat? The old way is dead for the informed person, but the new way isn't here yet.

This book is about what to do. We have outlined earlier our thoughts on "Certified Earth Foods," and on the next page you will find a reference chart describing again what they are, and what they do. This is a no-nonsense book, meant to make concrete suggestions as to what you should demand your supermarket and food chains bring to you, the consumer. Consumerism is the new movement of our generation, and it makes us all revolutionaries, if we take it seriously.

For ourselves and our children and grandchildren, we had better. Were you ever a revolutionary before?

This Is an Earth Food

An Earth Food is adequate, in its class of food, to nourish and please you because it was properly nourished itself in its production.

The sound and balanced processes of nature have been used in producing it, supplemented by the science and knowledge of man.

It will not poison or harm you, since harmful elements have not been used in its production, or in processing and preparing it for market.

It is produced in ways that recycle and use organic wastes, so they will not pollute precious lands and water.

It is produced under sound business contracts which see that the above conditions prevail, and that departures from them cannot be easily accomplished.

It has been analyzed in a competent independent laboratory for both its nutritional values and freedom from harmful elements, using practical sampling and testing procedures, and is certified as being suitable for human consumption.

It is called an Earth Food to designate that it is a safe and nutritious product, but a wide use of similar disciplines in producing and marketing good foods is advocated. The Earth Food model may be adapted for beneficial use by people everywhere.

CHAPTER ONE ✌

The Web
of Life

NATURE IS put together in families and clusters of living things. These groups help to feed and support one another in both simple and complex relationships. This is called the web of life and it must be seen as a whole to be fully understood.

When the coyote, for example, catches and eats rabbits, he helps all of the rabbits to live by adjusting their population to their living space and food supplies. It is the same with the wolves and the caribou they eat on the northern slopes of our continent. The wolves were never the true enemies of the caribou, and it is rather man who becomes their mortal foe due to his invasion of their environment. He disturbs their food chain and their web of life.

The lofty Douglas fir trees of a western forest, standing 150 feet high, filter sunlight and rain to all the plants and creatures below. The alders and vine maples then find their places to grow in half-shade, feeding on the forest litter of old limbs, twigs, bark, cones, needles, leaves and mosses that we call forest duff. Beneath the vine maples, the rhododendrons and devil's clubs grow, for them the shade and food supply is just right and the mild organic acids in the forest debris give them extra iron and boron for their special needs.

Then, under two arbors of shade and shelter, a myriad of things may grow: lilies of the valley, wild violets, trillium, huckleberries, maiden hair ferns, sword ferns, mosses, lichen, licorice roots, and millions of bugs, worms, nymphs and flies, even butterflies.

These are nature's neighbor plants, feeding each other and supporting all of the things that walk and crawl and swim and fly, acting as one another's waste disposal facilities.

The rivers and the sea receive the natural wastes from this land-life system. They get the surplus minerals not used by the plants and animals in the short term periods. Then they receive the massive loads of soils and debris as mountains erode into valleys and flat lands. The sea becomes a nutrient broth for all of the fishes and plants that live there. They bathe in every food material that is known on our planet: phosphorus, nitrogen, potassium, chlorine, calcium, sulphur, magnesium, manganese, iron, zinc, copper, boron, molybdenum, nickel, cobalt, iodine and dozens more that contribute to the nutrition of living things.

The plants and creatures of the sea evolve their own food chains. The herrings, for example, feed the larger meat-eating fish whose wastes support tiny plants that renew the cycle. The only actual waste is the energy of swimming and living, but the sun constantly renews the fuel supplies of the oceans. The plankton live on micro-plants and are in turn eaten by larger plankton which eventually feed the great whales.

The kelp of many colors and other sea weeds and grasses provide shelter for small fishes and food for the sapro-phytes that clean up the waste tissues at the end of the growing seasons. Then different food chains are formed where the oceans of the world meet their shore lines. These serve to clean up the wastes and dead tissues that are washed to the ocean edges. A massive garbage collection is handled by the shags, pelicans, mud hens, sea gulls and even the dainty sandpipers that patrol the beaches.

THE LIVING SOIL

The soil mantle of our earth has been produced by systems of life that are as complex as those of the sea. The magnitude of its population is hard to comprehend by people who usually do not think beyond millions. A spoonful of fertile soil, for example, may support over a billion bacteria, and the weight of the bodies of these tiny plant-creatures in an acre of good land may be over 1,200 pounds.

These bacteria live in colonies dependent upon their physical and chemical environment. The *azotobacter* colonies thrive in mildly acid soils and feed upon the vegetative wastes, while gathering nitrogen from the air to nourish the next growths of plants. Then the *clostridia* colonies take over in the soils that have a stronger acidity, but they are less efficient as nitrogen gatherers in this harsher chemical climate.

A bag of sulphate of ammonia applied to a fertile soil by a careless farmer can destroy the *azotobacter* colonies, and replace them with their less efficient cousins, because it increases the acidity reading.

The bacteria are joined by the fungi and algae as tiny tenants of the land. 90% of these little organisms live on the surfaces of the roots, supported by gentle chemical relationships that prevail there. In some instances the nutrition of the host plant is filtered through this living sheath. The bacteria act as the plant's feeders.

The fungi are by no means limited to being scavengers that feed off the dead tissues of plants. They also may develop mutually supporting relationships with their hosts. The *mycorrhizae* (literally, fungus root), for example, attach themselves to the roots of some kinds of plants, such as conifer trees, appearing as a grey web. This web then gathers nitrogen and transfers it to the living plant. Studies show that these fungi may double the nitrogen supplies for their hosts and thereby help them to grow.

These, however, are only the tiny organisms of the soil, the bacteria, fungi and algae. Their specialty is to work at the interface between the living and the dead. Consider also the springtails, mites, lice, nematodes, eelworms, weevils, earthworms, larvae, snails, and hosts of other bugs and insects, plus mice, moles, gophers and bigger creatures. Who is to say which are inherently beneficial and which are pests? Would you abolish any of the insects and worms, for example? Can you be sure they do not have a basic role in feeding you?

The earthworms are telltale messengers that the soil is fertile, and beware of the future of your colony if they ever fully disappear. They eat the soil, adding rich substances to it. Their manure, seen as funny little doolies in your yard and garden, is a cheerful sign. You know then that there is much more of it under the surface and your plants will surely grow.

Soil lives, and being alive, it regenerates itself in waves and cycles of reproduction, feeding, death, decay, feeding and reproducing again. The micro-organisms are basic to the process.

Robins and other small birds are indicators of the health of the life systems of temperate lands. They collect seeds, bugs, worms and tender shoots which in turn supply the teeming soil and the workshops of the bacteria, fungi and algae that live there.

DDT has been one of the major causes of disruption of

this delicate, interdependent web of life, as we discovered to our horror a few years ago.

Interestingly enough, bird watchers, rather than trained entomologists, were the first to notice that the community of the soil, bacteria, insects, plants and animals was in trouble because of the release of DDT into the environment.

Roland C. Clement, Vice President of the National Audubon Society, gave the following account of what happened to the House of Representatives committee reviewing the proposed Federal Pesticide Control Act of 1971.

The early signs of DDT damage to living community seemed unscientific to the chemists and control entomologists who dominated pesticides use in the last generation. It was doubly insulting to these people that bird watchers were the first to notice undesirable effects and complain about them. Birds, however, are often at the ends of long food chains and are therefore excellent barometers of what goes on in the environment. Birds are to the ecosystem what the canary once was to the coal miner, an indicator of unseen environmental deterioration.

Because the environment is complex, it takes years to ferret out the mechanisms that our technology so often upsets. The first red flag warning of ecosystem damage—one which went completely unheeded by the Department of Agriculture—was a 1958 discovery by Dr. Roy Barker of the University of Illinois that DDT applied to elm tree foilage in the early summer of one year killed robins the following spring because the earthworms had meanwhile consumed the elm foliage and abstracted and concentrated its DDT. Aso that year Dr. George J. Wallace of Michigan State College discovered massive robin mortality on his campus as a result of Dutch elm disease control programs, spoke to the annual Audubon Society convention about his findings, and published a preliminary report in *Audubon Magazine* (1959). This damage was abundantly confirmed by Hickey and Hunt (1960) in Wisconsin, and by Wurster et al. (1965) in New Hampshire.

In 1961 Dr. George M. Woodwell of the University of Maine showed that only 50 percent of aerially applied DDT was reaching its target. This was the first clue to the source of the DDT fallout that was confirmed around the world in succeeding years, in rain, in the snow of the Antarctic where it had never been applied (Sladen et al. 1966) and in the Atlantic trade winds and the oceans of the world (Risebrough et al., 1967, 1968).

In 1964 Dr. G. E. Burdick and his colleagues of the New York Conservation Department demonstrated for fish what Dr. Barker did for the elm leaf-earthworm-robin cycle in 1958. They found that DDT was transferred from the gravid female to her eggs and killed the young fish when these absorbed their yolk sac.

It is now evident to perceptive scientists that a sustained release of DDT and other long-lived poisons into our environment will obliterate whole communities and species of birds, animals and fish, simply through this process of transfer and concentration in the food chain. There is no assurance that ultimately humans could not be obliterated, too.

THE GREAT CORN BLIGHT

Nearly everyone has heard of the great U.S. corn blight that destroyed over 700 million bushels of our 1970 corn crop, with a commercial loss of about 1 billion dollars. If you haven't heard of it, just be patient, because the basic causes of this disaster are still with us and will continue to appear again and again in food crop news.

The little rascal that did the damage this time is named *Helminthosporium maydis, Race T.*, a virus. This means that if you had a million of them in a glass of water and then filtered it through porcelain, they would go right through the porcelain and come out on the other side still in the water. This shows that *Helmi* is quite small.

Helmi is particular about what he eats. He prefers the leaves and tissues of male sterile corn, of the varieties of hybrid corn that cannot pollinate themselves. Such corn was developed by our farm scientists to save the labor and cost of detasseling seed corn fields. All the farmer had to do with this male sterile variety was to bring in the desired kind of pollen for the cross-breeding and shake it on the silks and ears of his crop.

This kind of corn, however, is evidently in *Helmi's* food chain. He may have been waiting for 1,000 years for a good chance to feed and multiply on it. At any rate, when our cost-saving farmers planted miles of it in their corn-fields, *Helminthosporium maydis, Race T*. marched out and ate this part of the corn crop hardly touching the older fashioned open pollinated varieties.

What will he do in the future? No one knows. All we really know is that *Helmi* is with us and we cannot control him yet so growing such corn is no longer advisable.

THE DEER AND THE NEW ENGLAND WATERSHED

Ira Gabrielson, a farseeing ecologist when most of the university community would have been hard pressed to define the word, described an ecological system that illustrates how specialized, but basically logical, the life-supporting arrangements in nature may be. His wildlife studies showed how vital, for example, the feeding and movements of deer might be in nourishing, in turn, other living things. We shall construct a model, using one of his deer and mountainside situations, to describe how the various life forms may assist each other. Here is the model:

A New England river entered the ocean, supporting runs of Atlantic salmon in its two tributary rivers. The watershed of lean granite soils was originally in balance with itself and with its plants and animals, although it was not very productive.

A dam was built across one of the rivers. In a few years there were no deer left in that part of the watershed. Superficially, there seemed to be no good reason why they should leave, but here is what actually happened.

The food chain that included the deer was both biological and mineral. Not all of the fish returned to the sea after their spawning runs up the river. A substantial number died and left their dead bodies to fertilize the willows at the streamside. The willows consequently prospered and provided browse pastures for the deer.

The deer then carried food up the hills, discarding as they went calcium both in their droppings and in the annual shedding of their horns. Mice and other rodents gnawed the horns and the grasses took up the deer manure. The limited supply of calcium was then passed around the community. Its eventual movement, however, was always downhill and back to the river. The whole life system of this part of the watershed depended upon this annual income of calcium, and the deer vector to carry it back up the hills.

Stopping the salmon runs with the dam, starving out the willows, and eliminating the browse for the deer, the calcium carriers, broke the food chain and wholly altered the life and balance of this natural community.

This sort of thing may be a long series indeed, and very complex. The river also carried silicon to the sea, from the erosion of the granite rocks in the watershed. This silicon then could feed the tiny diatoms, the unicelled organisms that serve as primary links in the nutrition of all marine life. Somewhere in these systems, the calcium also contributed to growing the salmon that ran up the New England rivers to feed the willows, to feed the deer, who fed the mice and the grasses, and repaid the loan of the silicon from the granite rocks of this hard country.

Is there any reason to believe that our human webs of life are less elaborate, or less vulnerable, than this one of the deer?

It is accepted among the basic truths of life that security grows as many strands of supply are put into the community food systems, and that it declines when we over-simplify. A people with ten ways of getting carrots are more liable to have plenty, over the long run, than the people who rely solely on California's crop.

Our ways of life in the U.S. increasingly deny such basic truths. We live as if there were only two links in our food chain, the pay check and the supermarket, with no need for a complete waste disposal system.

Such a simplistic life style is unfair to our great, great grandchildren. They cannot speak, and one of our duties is to represent them in the big reweaving job of the next decade. We must learn to see sewage and trash as building blocks for new production, and the defiling of lands and water as crimes comparable to murder. If we get such vision, and then restore the quality in our own foods, we will have struck a blow for our great, great grand-children.

CHAPTER TWO ❧

Organic
Foods

THE WORD organic has acquired a generic meaning in our language, equivalent to safe and good, just as the word kleenex has been broadened to mean any kind of paper handkerchief. So organic foods are now considered safe and good by millions of Americans, while regular foods have become suspect as possibly contaminated with chemicals. This increasing suspicion among ordinary non-faddist customers about their food supplies is generating an amazing demand for organic foods.

The U.S. food industry brought this bad reputation for its products on itself. The big farmers used too much nitrogen to increase their yields, and thereby malnourished their crops. They used too many sprays, and the wrong kinds, to control insects, weeds and plant diseases. The food processors added too many and the wrong kinds of preservatives to increase the shelf life of food products, and they over processed the foods. The growers, processors and manufacturers progressively debased the quality of our foods in a misguided effort to produce huge supplies at lowest costs and highest profits, regardless.

The health and welfare of food consumers were neglected along the way in the headlong modernization of the U.S. food industry. Now the customers are revolting.

They are rejecting the main food offerings in the super-markets, and they are demanding organic foods. Why not? It is a natural reaction. Organic is the only word they know that means safe, good and wholesome in describing a food.

Let us look more closely at this popular term, organic food. How did we get to the place in American life where organic is one of the most exciting word symbols of our time?

The way to commence thinking about organic foods is to know that originally all foods were organic. They were produced with only the primary fertility and nutrition of nature. The decomposed leaves, roots, stalks, waxes, cells, colors and even smells of previous growth nourished the next year's crop. It was adequate nutrition, clearly, since it supplied exactly the same elements that produced the previous growth in the first place.

Such a natural way of growing plants and foods also has inherent safeguards against destruction of the crops by insects and diseases. The plants have centuries of built-in strength to resist local enemies. They are adapted to their climate and their places in the landscape. They are usually dispersed, mixed in with other species, so epidemics and invasions by insects cannot easily occur. Further, it is a production arrangement that has its own waste disposal system. It recycles and reuses last year's wastes to support the next year's growth. The wastes therefore do not accumulate in extraordinary quantities at undesirable places. Pollution of the environment is virtually unknown in areas that are unmolested by man.

Animals, birds, fishes and insects fit well into such a natural food supply system. They eat the organic plants, or each other, and get adequate nutrition since a complete provision of essential minerals is derived from the wastes.

23

These are built into the tissues of all the plants of a region, and then into the cells of all creatures that walk, swim and fly. No matter who bites what or who, the food is liable to be nutritionally good.

These balanced processes of nature make the super-pattern for organic farming and gardening in the United States and abroad. It is a food production system with these features: The crops are fertilized with organic wastes and earth minerals, so they may have access to whole cafeterias of the essential nutrients that make strong and healthy plants and good foods for people. The livestock and poultry are fed with these food-laden crops, so the good nutrition cycle is extended to them, and then to the people who consume the livestock and poultry products. Poison sprays and pharmaceuticals are not used in producing the crops and livestock. Good nutrition of the crops and sound ecological practices are used to keep insects and diseases under control. The animals are not confined in cages, feedlots and large colonies. They are allowed to graze and have exercise. The crops and livestock products are offered as human foods in their natural condition, with a minimum of processing, so the full nutritional values and the flavors may be received by the consumers.

This is an impressive food supply system. It is blessed with the traditions of Indians and later Americans who lived on our continent from the curtain of history until World War II. The Indian who fertilized his corn with a fish was only helping nature. He was an ecological man.

The farmers of America were organic while the nation was being built and until about 1920. They could not be otherwise, since modern farm chemicals had not yet been invented. They were practicing ecologists who recycled the manures and vegetable wastes of their communities back into the food chain as natural fertilizers. The chickens, pigs and cows walked on the earth and supplemented their diets with the bugs, weeds, roots and browse of nature.

One-fourth of all Americans lived on farms during our transition toward urbanization (1920-1940), so they ate some organic food every day. Another one-fourth, in the surrounding rural communities, got their meats, cereals and produce in the town and village stores. Their diets were significantly organic, being based upon dispersed and relatively simple systems of farming and food processing. If the butcher had added sodium nitrate to the meats to make them red and last longer, his neighbors might have lynched him. The pollution of foods, such as milk at that time, was from wholesome things that wouldn't kill you, like farm dirt.

Although the other half of the people lived in cities, it was unnecessary to extend the life of foods during long shipping and marketing periods. The bulk of the produce came from nearby production and processing places.

Consider this: Our earlier medium-sized cities, of 25,000 and 50,000, were supplied with meats, milk and fresh produce from nearby areas, and with breads and pastries from their own bakeries. But when the cities grew and became urban clusters, profound changes took place. The edges of the cities became so wide that dairying, poultry raising and vegetable and fruit farming got pushed into distant places. It then became expedient, in order to serve the urban markets profitably, to prolong the marketing and shelf life of the food products through pasteurization, chemical processing, adulteration, genetic selections of crops, modified embalming and cosmetic treatments. The farms were consolidated, progressively, into supply satellites for major food companies, with the result that farm-

25

ing, per se, was reduced to only a raw materials supply function, providing vegetable and animal tissues for the processors to convert over into durable food-like things. These changes in the food industry enabled the food companies to reach markets 1,000 miles away as easily as they had reached them when they were only 100 miles away. Freshness and natural quality were systematically removed from the consumers' value system. Not having had an honest apple or head of celery for 10 years, the customers forgot what good ones tasted like and of course the young would never know.

Let us illustrate all of this with some facts: fresh milk from Seattle and Portland has displaced most of the local supply for Fairbanks, Alaska; Wisconsin and Illinois milk moves freely into New York, Philadelphia, Washington, and New Orleans markets. The stabilized milk may be consumed by families ten days after it is taken from the cows.

The consolidation of production of vegetables and other produce has advanced to the point where 30% of all the nation's vegetables are now produced in California and 15% in Florida. They are shipped from these places in a biologically inactive condition into markets all over the country. The next time you pick up a tomato, a head of lettuce or a bottle of milk in the supermarket, handle it gently. It has had a long ride.

THE ORGANIC FOOD MOVEMENT

It is easy to see that organic farming, and a love of good organic foods, is not a recent event in America. It is rather that we started in the organic way and a massive change has taken place in recent years, mainly since 1940, that has put us on a dead end road.

The organic farmers and food customers are the survivors, rather than the new people. George Washington and Thomas Jefferson were organic farmers, and William Jennings Bryan is said to have died from over-eating because he liked organic foods so well.

Sir Albert Howard, an eminent Englishman who lived from 1873 to 1947 became the patron saint of organic farmers and food people world-wide, due to his work in advanced studies of agriculture both in England and India. He developed the Indore method of composting organic wastes, in which a skilled handling of the bulk materials and of temperature and moisture encourage colonies of bacteria to decompose the wastes.

Sir Albert observed, even at this early time, that malnutrition of plants and animals is the root cause of insect and fungus invasions, and ecologically sound farming is the essential remedy rather than the use of economic poisons.

This is an example of Sir Albert Howard's thoughts, from his *Agricultural Testament* which was published in 1940:

> Insects and fungi are not the real cause of plant disease, but only take unsuitable varieties of crops imperfectly grown. Their true role is that of sensors for pointing out crops improperly nourished—or keeping agriculture up to the mark. The policy of protecting crops from pests by means of sprays, cultures, and so forth, is unscientific and unsound, as often, when successful, such procedure merely preserves the unfit and obscures the real problem —how to grow healthy crops.

Sir Albert's second book *Farming And Gardening For Health And Disease* published in 1942 greatly stimulated the demand for organic foods, since it related good foods to human health, and poor foods to disease.

Mr. Friend Sykes, another great English farmer and a

friend of Sir Albert Howard, earned a companion role among world leaders in good food production. He cultivated 800 acres at Chantry, England, and producing strong race horses as well as organic crops.

Friend Sykes was an advanced ecologist, and he criticized the British trend toward specialized farming, including specialized farms for producing fine race horses. He found the horses often were malnourished and susceptible to diseases and said in *Food Farming and the Future* in 1950:

> The basic cause of our failure to beat the French horses is to be found in the quality of the food with which our animals have been fed during the past 12 years.
> What, then, is a sound basis for the establishment of a good feeding policy? Two words answer this question—Good farming. Of what does good farming consist? The farm entirely devoted to sheep becomes sheep-sick. A pure dairy farm has all the troubles that are going, and that land becomes cow-sick. The stud farm entirely devoted to horses is soon possessed of a soil which is horse-sick. In a pure and simple poultry farm the land becomes poultry-sick.

Friend Sykes went on to say:

> I have been farming for forty years, and during that time I have had, on my farm and on many of the farms where I have acted as an agricultural consultant, to deal with a number of outbreaks of diseases. These have not been cured in any one instance by the application of any known methods of veterinary or medical science. Disease . . . has only been eradicated by enlightened practice of good husbandry. This has pointed to mixed agriculture as the only basis upon which good farming can be conducted in England.

Friend Sykes was an early prophet of the DDT debacle and said in 1950, in the same book:

. . . I see accumulating evidence that the use of poisonous treatments for getting rid of insect pests and weeds may speedily prove to be a short-sighted and mistaken practice. . . .
The first thing that Nature does when she has been treated with poison is to battle against it and try to breed a resistant strain of the form of life that is being attacked. If the chemist persists in his poisonous methods, he often has to invent more and stronger poisons to deal with the resistance that Nature sets up against him. In this way, a vicious cycle is created. For, as a result of the conflict, pests of a hardier nature and poisons still more powerful are evolved; and who is to say that, in this protracted struggle, man himself may not ultimately be involved and overwhelmed? . . .

Our own American leader in organic farming and foods was J. I. Rodale of Emmaus, Pennsylvania, who died recently just as his views were finally gaining nationwide acceptance. "J.I.," as he was called over the years, launched *The Organic Farmer* magazine in 1942, with the encouragement of Sir Albert Howard, who served as an associate editor. This magazine stood against the U.S. poor food and bad farming trends for 29 years, under Rodale's challenging leadership, although he changed the name to *Organic Gardening And Farming* along the way, as independent farming declined. Rodale's companion magazine, *Prevention*, was launched in 1950, to serve organic and health food consumers.

The circulation of these Rodale magazines has climbed steeply since 1968, when an anxiety about food began to shake up U.S. consumers. *Prevention* now exceeds 1 million in circulation, and *Organic Gardening And Farming* has well over 700,000 subscribers.

All Americans owe a tribute to J. I. Rodale, regardless of whether they were his friends or foes, since he fought for the integrity of everyone's foods. He was a humorous man of many talents—in business, the theatre, farming and fighting the bad breath of big government. He was victorious over the Federal Trade Commission when they tried to stop the sale of his book *The Health Finder* because he advertised that it could "help the average person to remain comparatively free of many terrible diseases." FTC sued. Rodale fought the case for several years with the legal assistance of Thurmon Arnold, and marketed the books during the litigation. This battle over a principle cost J. I. Rodale over 200,000 dollars. Characteristically, he went for broke, and won.

The organic food market is currently a display of dramatic business growth, disorganization, whimsy, fraud, short supply, high prices and big time developments by major U.S. food companies as they try to respond to customer demands for better quality foods.

As a specific example of such a state of affairs, the Graber Produce Company of Ohio, one of America's truly competent and honest organic vegetable producers, recently plowed up some of its early season crops because the health and organic food stores were unable to claim them. Competent dealers and distributors who were able to receive trucklots did not exist in sufficient numbers to buy this precious merchandise. Still, the organic produce was selling in the retail stores at double the prices of conventional vegetables of the same kinds.

Fraud and misrepresentations of products as "organic" when they actually were not, have been disclosed in a number of cities, and it is suspected that this situation exists rather widely induced by high prices and a shortage of supplies. The United Fresh Fruit And Vegetable Association, based in Washington, D.C., has been investigating the authenticity of products in the organic markets. It reports many instances of mislabelling by dealers who simply removed or obliterated the original trade markings from conventional produce and displayed an organic claim or label.

Such unethical retailers are mainly newcomers. The older organic food community of the U.S. has a good reputation for civic responsibility.

A dramatic expansion of the health food business has contributed to these unsettled conditions. The present growth rate is about 30% per year, according to *Barrons Weekly*.[1] The annual retail volume for 1970 was about 140 million dollars (approximately $100 million wholesale) according to the W. T. Thompson Company. This market research firm estimates a rise to a 400 million dollar wholesale level by 1975, which might account for 570 million dollars worth in retail sales. This is big business.

Many capable food dealers and distributors, including perceptive chain store leaders, are responding to this expanding market. The Infinity Company of New York, for example, is expanding its organic grain milling and vegetable handling facilities, and diversifying its lines of merchandise. It is serving over 300 dealers and a number of supermarkets that are installing health food departments.

Shiloh Farms of Arkansas, an honest and capable supplier, is simply declining to accept additional customers pending production expansion, in order to sustain the honesty and quality of their products.

New Age Natural Foods in San Francisco has increased the number of its stores and also taken leadership in developing the Organic Merchants as a trade association to assist in surmounting supply and marketing problems.

The Ecological Food Society of New York has garnered

[1] *Barrons National Business & Financial Weekly*. May 10, 1971.

60,000 members who act as a buying club for organic and environmental merchandise. Their Ecology Mart is serving as the wholesale supply base for supermarket units as well as for health and organic food stores. The Society's sales for 1971 are estimated at about 1 million dollars.

Major chain stores are getting on the organic food bandwagon by assigning shelf space, or even whole departments, to the displays of such merchandise. The Safeway Stores company, organized in 24 divisions throughout the country, is leaving the decisions on installation of organic and ecological products to its divisional leadership. The national office at Oakland is deeply concerned, however, about misrepresentation of organic products and it will require rather stringent certifications of the integrity of such merchandise.

The consumers' co-operative food markets, such as Berkeley Co-op in California, Greenbelt Consumers based in greater Washington, D.C. and Mid-Eastern States in New Jersey, are accepting a leadership responsibility among U.S. food retailers to assure their customers that an upgrading of food quality will occur. Berkeley has already established an organic and ecological products department. Greenbelt, based in metropolitan Washington, D.C., is developing a special division to handle the whole range of organic, certified, safe and ecological products through its supermarket operations. Mid-Eastern is accepting a similar role of leadership and is also installing new fabricating and handling facilities for supplying their member co-operatives and consumer organizations.

The Rodale organization has held several regional meetings of organic food growers and processors, capped by a national organic food marketing symposium held recently at Allentown, Pennsylvania. The central theme is to assist capable growers and processors in expanding their production and in improving their marketing capabilities.

The chronic problem is a "mama and papa" kind of retailing where the individual stores can receive only small deliveries of goods. The transportation and distribution costs may then become excessive. A great deal of produce is being shipped from points of origin by air at costs running as high as 16¢ a pound.

These excessive marketing costs are a transitory feature of this trade, however, since the chain store competition will compel a better organization of the organic food business.

The organic and health food dealers are handling organic fruits and vegetables for a gross margin of about 33%, while a margin of 50% is common for conventional goods in supermarkets. Even so, the retail prices for the organic produce are usually half again higher than for nonorganic goods. Twice as high is not uncommon.

ORGANIC FOODS FOR TOMORROW

The ideology of the organic food movement in America has a healthy admixture of mysticism, as befits a strong folk movement. It is burdened, as well as served, with ideas and words that are a bit out of phase with reality. It is not a serious flaw, however, since the problems are mainly semantic.

The word "organic" for example, is a misnomer when applied to foods. All foods are organic, the good and the poor, the safe and the poisonous. The word "chemical" is also a misnomer. Nearly everything is chemical. Organic and chemical are not opposites, as we know from studying organic chemistry. Organic fertilizers are chemical, and so are inorganic fertilizers. The critical factor is the rate of solubility of each kind. The organic kind usually offer

33

their food to plants slowly and in better balance and variety. That is the main difference. Plants cannot tell whether the tiny fractions of nitrogen in the soil come from sulphate of ammonia or cow manure. If the plant can't tell, perhaps we have some more thinking to do about how to grow safe and good foods.

A more serious problem, however, is that of updating organic farming so it can work in our distorted world where wastes, business power and the demands of people are accumulating at the wrong places.

The manure piles and local debris are no longer behind barns and in fence rows. They are as big as mountains at the beef feeding lots and in the chicken factories and they are in the sewage and garbage collection systems of the big cities, mountains of them hundreds of miles away from the nearest farming areas.

Transitional policies and techniques will surely be needed to get these mountains of waste flowing back into the U.S. farming system. Even more basic is the fact that transitional guides will be needed to enable organic farmers and other good food growers to avoid bankruptcy while they produce for the clamoring customers of the cities.

These city customers, we believe, have an idyllic and unreal impression of any kind of farming in the U.S., to say nothing about organic farming. They visualize an idealistic corps of farmers driving their wagons through the communities gathering precious organic wastes, tending the compost piles, spreading the composts and manures on their crops, and picking the squash bugs off their plants by hand, or happily saying, "We grow enough for them, too," then hoeing out the weeds by hand. All this is for the health and safety of the city customers, and "the cause."

34

The fact is that conventional agriculture in the U.S. is a marginal industry that would lose all of its reported profit if it paid its hired hands a dollar fifty per hour. It is being run that way because it is an appendage of city-based food companies. There is no room in it anymore for independent family farmers who want to send their children to college. The wages are too low. The seemingly solvent farms are usually production units for companies whose managers don't care how low the prices of crops are at the farm gate. They'll get their profit between the gate and the grocery store.

This makes fierce competition for organic farmers, especially when they have to hire labor to haul the compost and tend the crops in the old fashioned way. A wage of 2 dollars per hour isn't enough to attract good workers and if the organic farmer cannot hire them he will have to exploit himself and his family to feed his city cousins, or go broke.

The sky-high prices for organic foods create a euphoria that this is a great business field for getting rich. This also is an illusion. The supermarkets are going full tilt into the organic food business, to serve their customers who are not noted for liking high prices and who, generally speaking, are non-faddists. They want safe, good food, not necessarily the ambrosia of heaven.

As the good foods move into the mainstream of American commerce for purchase by a wide variety of customers, we foresee changes.

The rigid rules of organic farming will be revised so less human labor will be needed and so costs can come down.

The ideas of balanced and complete nutrition of crops and animals will be accepted, along with the

35

present strictly defined "organic" ideas, and some carefully selected chemical fertilizers and crop protection materials will be used in growing "certified" food crops. This will enable the prices for safe and good food to come down some more.

Simple laboratory tests will be used to detect poisons in the soil and in the foods.

"Certified" safe and good foods will be available at about a 10% higher price than for the conventional products, and about 40% less than for strictly grown organic foods. The "certified" kind will supply most of the good food demand.

Organic food will stay in the markets, however, to serve the needs of discriminating customers.

Let us think of food as a spectrum. The finest and the purest are at one end; the worst at the other. Though we may never see truly pure foods again we must move to the positive side of the middle of the food spectrum again and perhaps inch our way up as we become more aware and more forceful as consumers.

CHAPTER THREE 🐦

A Carrot Is a Carrot Is a Carrot or Is It?

AMERICAN agriculture has been dominated for the past 30 years by a yield-happy fraternity of farm scientists who have advocated, basically, that a carrot is a carrot is a carrot, regardless of where or how it is grown. They have been armed with hired fieldmen, nitrogen factories and supermarket contracts to prove their contentions, which might be summarized as follows: There is not much difference between one good-looking carrot and another good-looking carrot. If there is a nutritional difference between the carrots, it doesn't matter much, anyway. Just eat some more if you are still hungry. You cannot get more money for better carrots, so why grow better ones? Just grow lots of good-looking carrots.

Luckily the farm scientists of this persuasion in and out of the Department of Agriculture have finally been placed on the defensive, and they are now doing some re-thinking. A stimulus for this has been the recent evidence that all is not well on the U.S. food scene. Even the affluent food customers are showing signs of malnutrition.

Additional stimuli for the backtracking of these pseudo-scientists is the plain fact that a carrot is not a carrot is not a carrot. And that two carrots, grown differently, may even be as different food-wise as carrots and turnips. The same truth applies to tomatoes, potatoes, apples, melons, milk, wheat, rice, eggs, meats and all other natural foods.

This subject is so basic in developing a sound national food and nutrition system that we shall present it in some depth, stating essential principles and then offering illustrations to assist in their understanding.

First, however, we will cite two quotations from past and present food program leaders to indicate the lack of guidance that is prevalent.

Some persons advocate the theory that the food value of crops grown on depleted soils is poor, and that plants are devitalized or demineralized, or otherwise deprived of natural nutrients because they have not been grown according to the principles of organic farming.

This subject has been investigated by the Plant, Soil And Nutrition Laboratory in Ithaca, N.Y. . . . Research at the laboratory gives no evidence that the composition of the crops grown is essentially different as a result of the kind or amount of commercial fertilizer used on the soil. Lack of fertilizer may reduce the yield of a crop, but not the amount of nutrients in the food produced.—(Dr. Helen Mitchell, then Dean, School Of Home Economics, University of Massachusetts. *FOOD, USDA Yearbook.* 1959.)

Our tables of food composition would be of little or no value if the composition of a plant were dependent on the composition of the soil in which it was grown. It is the yield per acre that is greatly influenced by the kind and extent of fertilizer used. Composition is controlled by hereditary factors or genes which also control other characteristics of the plant such as size and shape. Thus we find that the seemingly plausible preaching that depleted soils produce foods of poor nutritional quality and that this is the basis for extensive supplementation of minerals and vitamins has no basis in scientific fact.—

A Carrot Is a Carrot Is a Carrot or Is It?

Dr. E. M. Nelson, then Chief, Nutritional Division, Food And Drug Administration. From *1959 Department of Agriculture Yearbook.*

These two statements, which reflect current views in the Department of Agriculture and the Food and Drug Administration, are out of phase with reality as a belief that the world is flat.

The fact is that neither plants nor men, nor even a grain of salt, can violate a basic law of thermodynamics, which says: "The sum of matter and energy in a closed system is constant."

This means, simply that a plant cannot contain any element that has not been present in the air or the soil in which it grew. It means that a plant grown in a soil that is deficient in iron, calcium, cobalt, or manganese cannot produce these elements, so its tissues will be deficient in them. The eminent authorities just quoted, who said the opposite, *are wrong* and the prevailing views in their agencies to this effect *are wrong*. The food values of crops *are* controlled by fertilizers, climate, soils and the methods of growing those crops, as well as by their heredity!

CONGRESSMAN KING AND THE HIDDEN FDA MEMO

Congressman David S. King (Utah) brought the issue of varying food values in crops into an interesting light in 1965 when he compelled the Food and Drug Administration to reveal that basic differences of opinion existed among its own staff leaders. This occurred when the Congressman questioned FDA's report on medical quackery which stated that "nutritional values of our crops are not significantly affected by either the soil or kind of fertilizer used," restating its official, and still current, position.

The story of what then happened is told in the *Congressional Record* (pages 3200-3204, February 16, 1966, House portion) under the caption "Deception By Various Federal Agencies," by Mr. King. He said to his colleagues in the House of Representatives:

> Mr. Speaker, I am alarmed at the lack of cooperation and the secretiveness, even the willful deception, that is currently practiced by various Federal agencies.
>
> It is conceded, I believe, that one of the most effective bulwarks of freedom in the United States has been our historic resistance to government in secret. Yet there is evidence, today, that secretiveness has become in some instances an instrument of departmental policy. . . .
>
> Now that the government is spending billions of dollars in basic research—which amount represents over 60 percent of all basic research conducted in this country—it is mandatory that this information be made freely available to the public. People are entitled to this dearly paid for information, not as a matter of grace, but as a matter of right, subject only to the considerations of national security. . . .
>
> Over the past 8 months I have had a most frustrating experience with the Food and Drug Administration. Personnel of that agency have followed a policy of official deafness and calculated obtuseness that defies credibility.

Congressman King then goes on to relate that he arranged a meeting with Dr. Phillip L. Harris, then Director of the Nutrition Division of FDA, and Dr. Homer Hopkins, a food research officer of the same division. He questioned FDA's statement that the food values of crops are unaffected by soils and fertilizer practices. As a result of this discussion, Dr. Harris agreed to make a reassessment of the situation, and of existing research in this field.

It happened that Dr. Homer Hopkins was given the assignment to assist in this review; and he produced a scientific memorandum on the subject dated June 11, 1965 and entitled "Report On The Question Of Soils And Fertilizers In Relations To The Quantity And Chemical Composition Of Foods Of Plant Origin, And Other Questions" which was reprinted in full in the *Congressional Record*, House portion, February 16, 1966.

Dr. Hopkins said in this memo, addressed to Dr. Harris, that the FDA statement "cannot be defended." He pointed out that "too few well designed, all-encompassing experiments in human nutrition have been conducted in the United States, over sufficiently long periods of time, to fully document the generalization that 'the nutritional values of our crops are not significantly affected by either the soil or kind of fertilizer used.' " He cited evidence from 15 U.S. and foreign research reports that fertilizers and soils did, indeed, influence the mineral composition of plants, and, in turn, the animals that consumed the plants. His citations included instances where: 1) adding nitrogen fertilizers in Mississippi lowered the calcium contents of turnip greens; 2) adding calcium carbonate (lime) increased the calcium contents of crops in North Carolina; 3) adding boron to boron-deficient soils caused an increase in chlorophyll and carotene contents of alfalfa in North Carolina; 4) adding phosphorus to deficient soils increased the phosphorus contents of soy bean plants; 5) adding nitrogen and potassium fertilizers doubled the thiamine contents of oats and millet; 6) increasing the sulphur in the root zones of two alfalfa strains approximately doubled the methionine and cystine contents of the plants; 7) feeding rats on turnip greens from a cobalt-deficient soil in Georgia depressed their growth, due to an absence of Vitamin B^{12} in the greens from such soils; 8) feeding animals on grass from lands heavily fertilized with potassium caused tetany in the animals.

The FDA tried to conceal Dr. Hopkins' report. They

41

"classified" it. Congressman King tried repeatedly, from July through September of 1965, to get a copy of this document, but, as he says in the *Congressional Record*, "the curtain of silence fell."

Finally, the Congressman received the following letter from W. B. Rankin (now deceased), then the number two man in FDA, about Dr. Hopkins' scientific memorandum:

October 20, 1965

Dear Congressman King:

This is in response to your letters of October 5, 1965 and October 6, 1965, and our telephone conversation this morning.

We have been reviewing the available scientific literature regarding the relationship between the nutritive qualities of foods and the chemical composition of the soil upon which these foods are grown. We have found no scientific evidence to indicate that there is any significant effect on the nutritive level of the U.S. dietary which can be related to the nutritive level of crops grown upon different soils. The iodine content of some foods is influenced by soil composition but this is of no practical significance at this time.

This reaffirms our present position on this entire matter. This position is in agreement with the views of our Dr. Homer Hopkins.

Sincerely yours,
W. B. Rankin
Assistant Commissioner
For Planning

Congressman King replied on October 21, 1965:

Dear Mr. Rankin:

I have just received your letter of October 20.

Would you please send me by return messenger a copy

of the Interoffice Scientific Memorandum by Dr. Homer Hopkins dated about June 11, 1965, so that I can determine for myself whether or not your most recent letter accurately reflects Dr. Hopkins' views.

Sincerely yours,
David King

Rankin did not answer, nor did Commissioner George P. Larrick (now deceased) when Representative King pursued his request by telegram on November 15th. The Congressman then requested John W. Gardner, Secretary of HEW, to compel FDA to provide him with Dr. Hopkins' memo. FDA complied, using two messengers, on November 30, 1965.

We have recited this series of events because repressive thought control within the Food and Drug Administration and the Department of Agriculture is part of the problem in restoring safety and quality of foods in America. This can be dispelled only through vigorous consumer activity which, in effect, fully counterbalances the influence of food producers and processing companies. These agencies have hundreds of capable and modern-minded personnel who are prepared to respond to consumers' needs in their various assignments. Dr. Hopkins was just one example of such a person.

The scientific procedures for checking the nutritional status of crops are so well developed in the U.S. that whole books are written on the subject. Thousands of scientists and technicians make literally millions of sap and tissue tests on all kinds of crops each year. The USDA assists in making such tests although it still officially denies their validity when their results are generalized into the fields of foods and human nutrition.

A growing plant may be likened to a factory with con-

43

veyor belts running to it, carrying in all of the essential materials for making complex products. One carries nitrogen, another phosphate, and still others zinc, copper, boron, and calcium. If any of the belts are empty, the end product will have missing parts.

The sap of the plant is the conveyor system, of course, bringing the building materials from the roots and leaves into the plant's cells and its growing tissues. Our first method of checking the nutrition of a plant for the minerals it is getting is a sap test to examine this vital fluid. We have portable testing equipment for making such tests in the field, to see how the plants are being nourished as they grow. It is a simple procedure requiring only 20 minutes.

The plant forms its soft tissues from the nutrients in the sap. Our next kind of a test is a tissue test to determine the actual composition of these tissues. Samples are collected from suitable places on the plants, bushes or trees, such as leaf tissue next to a developing ear of corn. This material can then be dried in an oven and used in a dry matter analysis of its mineral composition, the minerals it may eventually offer you as a food.

The plants also lend themselves to still another kind of analysis called an ash test. In this test the plant samples are burned in a very hot oven. All of the matter such as hydrogen and oxygen that came from the air in the growth of the plant then returns to the air, and only the minerals that came from the soil remain as the ash. We can analyze this ash and tell exactly what minerals the plant was able to gather in its growth. It is a bit more exact than a dry matter test.

A typical example of a modern farm service agency that performs tissue tests to assist farmers in their crop production is the Ohio Plant Laboratory, based in Wooster, Ohio. This laboratory, which is a part of the Ohio State University system, serves thousands of Ohio farmers, as well as serving non-profit organizations of neighboring states. A major activity is running tissue tests on corn crops. The procedure is to take tissue samples from the ear leaves of the corn plants, that is from the leaves next to developing ears of corn, and to check these for mineral content, in order to determine the nutritional status of the various fields. Such samples are not segregated by varieties of corn, but represent a cross section of all kinds of corn grown in the State.

The results of the 1965 corn field tests for minerals in the plants, made by this laboratory, were summarized and published in the *Soil Science Society Journal*, Volume 2, 1967. They showed these variations in the amounts of iron, copper and zinc: The iron contents in the various samples ranged from less than 10 parts per million to more than 250 parts per million. The copper contents varied from 2 parts per million to over 50 parts per million. The zinc contents enjoyed a ten fold range, from 10 to 100 parts per million.

Such variations in the mineral composition of corn plants could be explained on the basis of the heredity of the plants; that is, that "X" variety had the very low 10 parts per million of iron, while "Y" variety had the high 250 parts per million, etc. Such a theory is unnecessary, however, since we know from similar experience that the soils and fertilizer practices in these different corn fields had a major influence upon the mineral composition of the plants. The official views of the Department of Agriculture and the Food and Drug Administration are wrong, when they contend otherwise.

45

This view is supported by the work of the late Dr. Firman E. Bear, an eminent scientist, who served as head of the Soils Department at Rutgers University in New Jersey for many years. Dr. Bear recognized the significance of good agriculture as the basis for adequate human nutrition. He first helped farmers to use soil and tissue analysis in improving their yields of crops, and then later he turned his attention to the companion research—that the levels of mineral content in the crops had a significant role in nourishing people. He launched a project that dealt specifically with those variations in the mineral contents of vegetables, which might be important to the people who ate them.

Dr. Bear made arrangements to get samples of vegetables from various production areas in 10 states. He limited these samples to identical varieties of the different vegetables, making sure that they were taken at the same stage in the growth of the plants. He narrowed the differences to those of soil, fertilizer treatment and climate.

After collecting the samples of vegetables, Dr. Bear analyzed the mineral contents with a cathode ray machine. He demonstrated, in this way, the wide variations that existed in their mineral composition, and in the food values that they represented. He showed that two similar looking tomatoes—or snap beans, lettuce, cabbage or spinach— might vary as much as 1000% in mineral values. He proved that the official views of the Department of Agriculture and the Food and Drug Administration in these matters were wrong.

The body of Dr. Firman Bear's work in this project was published in the *Proceedings of the Soil Science Society of America*, Volume 13, 1948, under the title "Variation in Mineral Composition of Vegetables."

Kind of Vegetable	Total of Mineral Matter as a Percent of Dry Weight	
	Highest	*Lowest*
Snap beans	10.5%	4.0%
Cabbage	10.4%	6.1%
Lettuce	24.3%	7.0%
Tomatoes	14.2%	6.1%
Spinach	28.6%	12.4%

The detailed information on variations in vital food elements was impressive. The iron contents of tomatoes, for example, varied from 1 part per million in the poorest up to over 1,900 per million in the best. The calcium levels in the lettuce varied from 16 millequivalents in the poorest up to 71 in the best, a difference of over 400%. The copper in spinach ranged from 12 parts per million in the low sample up to 88 in the highest. Cobalt, a vital element in human nutrition, was entirely absent in the poorer samples of beans, cabbage, lettuce and tomatoes, and barely present in the poorer spinach, although significantly present in the more mineral-rich samples.

These tremendous variations in the food values of vegetables raise the questions: What does the consumer really get for his hard earned money at the vegetable and fruit counters in the food markets? Do the vitamin values vary this much, too?

The nation cannot afford the nonsense of such widely varied food values which are a result of agriculture's becoming a factory operation wherein the original qualities of the vegetables and fruits are being obliterated by the ways the crops are produced.

MODERN FARMING MAGNIFIES
THE FOOD QUALITY PROBLEM

The old fashioned family farmer has virtually disappeared from the U.S. scene as a viable producer and at least 80% of the crops and meat products pour out of the fields and feedlots using modern factory methods. A typical vegetable operation in California, Texas or Florida may grow three crops a year in the same field in a soil that is beat, molded, rilled, hilled, gassed, anointed, treated, watered and harvested with complete disregard for the bacteria and microcreatures that once lived there.

The corporate farmer will use only those fertilizers that give increases in yield and in the grade of the crops. This means that the fertilization is usually limited to nitrogen, phosphate and potash, plus a few other elements that must be used lest the plants die or become unmarketable. It is a grim system, as far as the nutritional interests of consumers are concerned.

The basic idea, so long advocated by USDA, that the soil will supply all of the secondary and trace minerals that might be needed, along with the nitrogen, phosphate and potash, cannot be supported in such a system. These critical minerals for building nutritive values in the foods simply cannot be supplied fast enough by the depleted bacteria in these soils to enrich the crops, and in turn, to nourish you.

The lowly carrot may some day be placed in the Smithsonian Institution as the vegetable that broke the back of food science bigotry in the U.S. Its value, authorities say, is in its carotene (Vitamin A), yet we suspect that future research will show that carrots have whole "personalities," with carotene linked to their enzymes, and their enzymes linked to their copper, this linked to zinc, both to the nitrogen, and then laced over to the auxins, and then to the giberelins, the colors and the smells, just like your collarbone, neckbone, shoulderbone, backbone, legbone and shinbone.

We suspect, in other words, that the same kind of good

farming that will restore earth minerals in our food crops will also assure the adequacy of the vitamins, and the mystical vapors that the gourmet and health food people dream about. Frankly, we find more sense in their mysticism than in USDA's outdated attitudes. There is still more to be found out about growing good foods in human production systems that we have ever discovered to date.

Each basic food item has certain key values that, in the minds of informed customers, make it worth buying. If those values are actually not present, he gets cheated. In the case of oranges and orange juice, for example, the customer buys it for vitamin C and other plus values, not for protein or because the orange has a pretty golden color.

It would be possible to rate oranges and orange juice for four key factors and thereby assure an informed customer that he is getting a good product. Such a rating might certify, for example: The vitamin C (ascorbic acid) content: that it is above a selected level, for nutritional value. The sugar-acid ratio (Brix test), for flavor. The total solids as a per cent of the total weight—that there is no excess water in a fruit's bulk, but that it's all fruit—as a further criterion of quality. A relative freedom from DDT or other harmful chemicals, for safety.

A sound production program does not assure that the vitamin and flavor levels would be in the product for the consumer, since harvesting, care and transport are then involved. It can assure, however, that the building blocks for quality are in the crop. The costs of producing such premium oranges, based upon a complete nutrition of the crop, would not be more than 5% above the costs in conventional dead-level cultivation and the long range costs might not be any more.

Up-to-date farm and food scientists are prepared to suggest reasonable guides for such a production program, dealing with key quality and value factors for vegetables, fruits, grains and for crop products, such as fruit and vegetable juices. The research data that has been accumulating for 30 years, in crop production testing, is available for use in a system that deals with the nutrition of people, as Dr. Firman Bear illustrated.

Equally good guides are available for vitamin analysis, and for detecting an excessive presence of harmful chemicals in food crops, such as DDT, arsenic and mercury. Gas chromatograph equipment is capable of detecting and measuring these factors.

The elements of a sound food crop production and rating system are available. The research guides are adequate. An abundance of skilled technical people, capable of performing the essential services, is scattered over the country, in all crop producing regions. A magnificent challenge exists in the demands of food rebels for better supplies of good and safe foods. They are willing to pay the price, and it will not be much more, even in the short run. All of this adds up to a combined civic and business opportunity.

The biggest single hurdle, however, is the psychological one, to get rid of the idea, once and for all, that a carrot is a carrot is a carrot and that modern mechanized agriculture is God's finest gift to man, which will save us all from starvation. Modern agriculture may suffocate us with its manures instead.

IRON AND THE PEOPLE OF NEW YORK

This topic, the nutritional content of food, is so vital to every reader that we should create a strong illustration that people may remember.

All of the people of New York City, men, women and

children, weigh about 1 billion pounds. Approximately 10 tons of this total, 20,000 pounds, is the iron of their body tissues. This iron is a precious thing. It makes the enzymes that control New Yorkers even more effective than the police. It also makes the hemoglobin of their blood, that carries oxygen so they can breathe. Without iron, New Yorkers would have anemia and die. National health and nutrition surveys show that a rising number of Americans, especially women, have anemia, the lack of essential iron. The people of New York also have this problem, in part due to the poor quality of their food supplies. Profit-hungry producers go for high yields, not caring for the nutritional quality of the foods they ship into New York. This poor quality should be stopped. The full nutritional values of foods should be restored, so New Yorkers may again have an adequate iron supply in the foods that are shipped into that city. This 10 tons of iron in the 1 billion pounds of New Yorkers must be replaced in order to maintain the level, because they lose a great deal of iron every day. They need this so they can endure, and handle their other problems, which seem to get larger all the time.

New Yorkers and all other Americans may be assured that all of the essential scientific and technical resources are at hand for guiding the production of rated and certified foods, those that are clearly safe and superior for human consumption. We are ready. The quality of the products must be maintained for the army of shoppers who are demanding safe foods that taste good, and are good.

Let the old leaders in the Food and Drug Administration and the Department of Agriculture fret over the heredity of crops. The younger men will soon take over, anyway. And someday, one of the old guard will ask for a carrot. We'll say, "Which one?" He'll say, "Oh, that one with the certified tag on the bunch. They taste better." Then we'll say, "That's no tag, that's the rating. It's got at least 12,000 units of vitamin A; some bonus factors, and it hasn't got any aldrin in it."

We'll know then that a carrot is no longer a carrot is no longer a carrot, but is a fit symbol for better eating in the United States.

The Land

Henry George, United States economist and land reformer (*1839–1897*) discovered that the value of land is measured by the number of people who passed the front gate each day. If one came by, your place might be worth $1,000; if 100 came by, it could be $100,000. Even your gold mine might be worthless if no one could possibly travel past your land.

"So," he said, "the people give you the value of the land, and the people may take it away. Blessed are the people."

"Also," he said, "Landowners are only custodians. They are the users of the land. If they use it well, they may keep it. If they use it poorly, the people should take it back again, and let a good custodian have it."

The feudal kings, using a similar theory, granted fiefs of land to chosen feudal lords. The people who lived there were also given to the lords, as serfs. But again, there

53

was a string attached. The lord was only a custodian. He could retain the land and the serfs only as long as he cared for them well. If he abused the land or failed to feed the serfs and give them social security, the king could reclaim the fief and give it to a better lord.

God, as the partner of feudal kings, approved these transactions.

Do not smile. Feudalism worked as well in relation to its original ideals as democracy works in relation to our Bill of Rights. Remember, in the ancient ceremony of knighting the feudal lord, a lowly serf hit him across the face with a glove, to remind him all over again that he must serve the whole community, caring for the land and feeding the people, or lose it all.

Are we so proud?

Who cares for our land? Who cares for our people? Who intervenes when bad farmers pollute the land and hurt the communities?

The farmer's eye should fatten the cattle. His dreams should sow the crops. His mind should fertilize the soil. His love should attend the harvest.

Where have America's farmers gone? Will they ever return?

Growing Earth Foods

GROWING EARTH FOODS is only using the powers of nature along with human knowledge to produce foods that suit good specifications and then using these farming operations in recycling the organic wastes of our communities. Both features are equally important, the good food part and the waste disposal part, because our modern communities, just like modern houses, get unliveable when their plumbing systems don't work. Nothing is worse than an overflowing toilet bowl, especially when it gets into your drinking water. Ours, collectively, is at that point.

Achieving the first objective, growing healthy plants and animals, is not too difficult from a technical standpoint. We have sufficient skills for doing this. We are capable, for example, of changing the scent of a rose by changing its diet, increasing the vitamin C of tomatoes by regulating the supply of sunlight, improving the flavor factors of mint leaves, so they will make better chewing gum, controlling the flavor contents of hops, from which to make beer, altering the sex of roosters so they can lay eggs, and of hens so they can crow, growing green color in lawn grass by providing magnesium and iron, changing the color of apples by regulating their potassium supplies, making stubborn rhododendron plants grow buds and blooms by

55

regulating the carbon-nitrogen ratio in their sap and changing the quality of milk and eggs by selections of the cows and hens, but also by changing their diets.

If we can do such things, and we surely can, we are able to grow farm crops and animals that will adequately feed you. Fortunately, the cost is reasonable. It is as cheap to have good tomatoes and oranges as poor ones.

HOW PLANTS GROW

Corn plants have been companions of people for centuries. Let us use them as examples of how plants grow. These plants are made of about 40 different earth minerals gathered from the soil, plus supplies of nitrogen, hydrogen, oxygen and carbon gathered from air and water.

The corn plant breathes in the carbon and oxygen from the air, in the form of carbon dioxide. It sucks in the hydrogen and oxygen in the form of water through its roots. It gathers in the earth minerals as tiny particles (ions), using its roots. And it borrows nitrogen from the soil's organic supplies, again using its roots.

The sun, however, is the plant's god. It works the miracles. Its light shines on the corn leaf, starting with the first tiny one, and presto, this changes the water and carbon dioxide of the leaf into sugar. This is done using the sunlight, in the chlorophyll cells of the leaves. It is the basic event of life, rather like a botanical nativity. Sugar is born from the marriage of water and carbon dioxide, in green corn leaves, using the radiance of the sun.

Now we are in business! We have sugar to use with earth minerals and nitrogen in making every conceivable kind of vegetable product. The corn plant, itself, is the wizard factory for these fabrications. It can make all sorts of things. It can convert the sugar into starch and into other carbohydrates. It can hook nitrogen atoms into the carbohydrates and make about 23 different kinds of amino acids, and then combine these, in all sorts of criss-cross ways, in making vegetable proteins. It can fabricate fats, waxes and resins. It can make cellulose fibers, and the lignin to glue them together, so the plant will stand tall and straight. It can create its own genetic history, in the embryo of the seeds, to ensure that the corn family will endure. It can make and use hormones that decide what kinds of cells will grow, which buds will become leaves, and which ones will become tassels and ears.

The corn plants have regulators for these various growth operations. The enzymes which always contain at least one earth mineral, govern the chemical reactions within the cells of the plant. The auxins govern the cell division and growth.

What we see here, in the corn plant, is a beautifully adjusted mechanism for gathering raw materials and making them into valuable products, useful to animals, birds and insects and useful to people as food.

PLANTS IN NATURE AND WITH PEOPLE

Plants maintain an integrity of relationships which generally protects them from distorted growth. The earth minerals, mined by bacteria and weathering of rocks, are given sparsely to the roots in ratios that relate to the natural supplies. The nitrogen must filter in through the processes of decay, never as a deluge. The water is regulated by climate and the seasons, and the air is always there.

A plant can starve or die of thirst in such a system, but it will not, as a rule, get fed out of shape or have chronic malnutrition. Those maladies appear only when people come on the scene and manage the crops. It is the heavy handed farmer with his truck load of nitrogen that does the plant in.

Look at this from a worm's eye view. Here comes the farmer with a bucket of fertilizer, not 20 plantfoods in good proportions, nor 12, nor 6, but 1, 2, or 3, always nitrogen, phosphorus and potash (NPK), and mostly nitrogen. He spreads it on the corn field. What has he done? He has created a mineral imbalance in the soil and malnutrition in the plants, by forcing new growth with only one-tenth of the essential foods.

The Department of Agriculture has encouraged and served this kind of unbalanced farming over the years because the unbalanced fertilizer practices developed slowly, without creating conspicuous disorders, and they dramatically increased yields and lowered costs of the nation's food supplies.

USDA has had a theory about all of this. It has held that the soils had abundant accumulated supplies of most of the earth minerals, varying from area to area, to be sure, but generally sufficient for years of farming to come. Nitrogen was therefore the main item to be added to stimulate increased crop yields, with phosphate, potash, magnesium, zinc, boron and a few other foods to be added therapeutically as indicated by soil analyses. They relied on the heredity of the plants, as we saw earlier, to sustain the quality of the crops.

The applications of these simplistic fertilizers, ignoring a balanced nutrition of crops and livestock, have risen steadily for 30 years. In 1970, the quantities and outlays were:[2]

[2] Fertilizer Group, Economic Research Service, U.S. Department of Agriculture. 1971 report from unpublished data.

Total commercial fertilizers used ...... 38.3 million tons
Total nitrogen fertilizers used .... 11.8 million tons
Total actual elemental nitrogen
    contained in the above fertilizers ..... 7.5 million tons
Total cash outlays for commercial
    fertilizers used in U.S. farming ...... $2 billion

The sheer quantities of these nutrients used in producing crops is not the essence of the problem, nor is it the fact that they are chemicals. The disorder in producing food and forage crops is rather in their malnutrition, a failure to achieve a balance in the nutrients applied, and particularly in failing to associate the nitrogen with sufficient quantities of other essential plant foods.

NITROGEN: THE KING IN
PRODUCTION AND POLLUTION

Nitrogen, among the 20 or more foods that plants use in their growth, has a special place. It is used in the largest quantities in relation to the other foods, and it has the leading role in making amino acids and proteins. No matter what kind of a plant it may be, wheat, rice, lettuce, apple, clover, carrot, rose, corn or bean, nitrogen accounts for over half of the nutrients used in its full growth cycle. The others will comprise the remainder.

Nitrogen is also the chief actor in the nitrogen cycle which enabled life to commence on our earth in the first place, and steadily supports it. It is this vital operation in which the bacteria of the soil capture nitrogen from the air, feed it to plants and thence to all living things, and then recover it from animal and vegetable wastes to support other cycles of life and growth.

Nitrogen is the king of the plant foods. It is also the key factor in the waste disposal system of Space Ship Earth. It

59

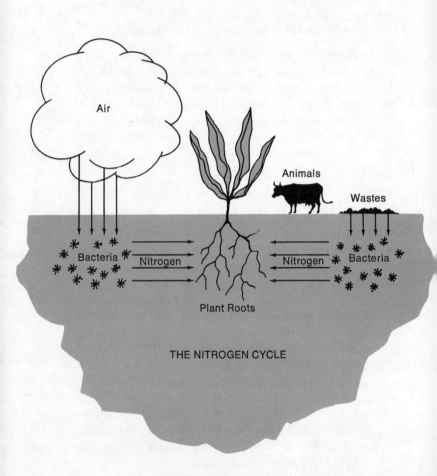

Air

Animals

Wastes

Bacteria   Nitrogen   Nitrogen   Bacteria

Plant Roots

THE NITROGEN CYCLE

is a morbid food for plants and animals when fed in an unbalanced fashion or too fast, but the greatest when properly used. It is the wild element in our environment, that can destroy land, water and people when pushed outside of its natural cycle, but the regenerator of life when it is allowed to support new crops, turf and trees.

The transgressions of modern farmers in growing food crops are their misuse of nitrogen and other major nutrients, not in their use of them in chemical or atificial forms. The transgressions of our cities and food industry in polluting the environment with organic wastes are due to persistent interruptions of the disposal cycles of nature, causing nitrogen to be released into the environment as a wild force, rather than being harnessed usefully in the further production of crops.

EARTH FOOD FARMING MATERIALS

We seek to establish a broader view of organic farming, so the guides of nature can be used successfully in a crowded society. We seek to modernize and render workable in a dollars-and-cents way the sound principles of cycle farming. The end products, of course, will be good and safe foods.

Sufficient discussion has been given in the previous chapters so readers can visualize the natural ways of growing plants and animals, the goals that we should strive to achieve:

Complete diets are needed, if this requires fertilizing with a dozen or even twenty elements.

Balanced feeding is essential, not just additions of NPK or what gives highest short run yields and profits.

Gentle and controlled nutrition is needed, rather than floods and flushes of the essential foods.

A cycling of the organic wastes back into the growth processes is essential, to sustain the fertility of the land and also to dispose of the wastes.

These guides, emulating nature, can be expressed in farming operations that use combinations of organic and inorganic fertilizers to nourish the crops. Good farmers are willing to use full nutrition fertilizers, and recycling practices, if the costs are made reasonable. The public is ready to buy the products, since they will be superior foods at reasonable prices.

Here are some of the materials that are available for full diet farming. Some of them, you will notice, are made of organic wastes, and will start a flow of these wastes back into agriculture:

Feather meal, a superior fertilizer and feed material, is made from poultry production wastes. It contains about 10% nitrogen.

Seaweed meal houses sufficient nutritional elements so that nothing could be missing in a modern full-diet fertilizer.

Fritted trace elements describes a slow-feeding form of the principal trace elements (iron, zinc, manganese, copper, boron and molybdenum), that would be enough for a balanced fertilizer. The elements are released slowly to plants by action of soil bacteria.

Ureaform is a slow-acting synthetic organic nitrogen material. It has 38% nitrogen, of which only 1% is soluble. It, too, is released by soil bacteria.

Leached langbenite, an earth mineral from old sea deposits, after removal of excess salt, has good supplies of potassium, magnesium and sulphur.

Bone meal, a familiar plant food from meat processing wastes, contains over 20% phosphate and a healthy cargo of calcium. It is gentle and slow acting.

Composted feed lot manure may be dried and screened to a desirable texture for immediate use, or for further processing as described below.

Composted sewage sludge may also be processed as a likely fertilizer material.

Fish and crab wastes are high in nitrogen and secondary nutrients. They can be processed into high grade fertilizer materials, and also into superior liquid fish fertilizers for foliar applications.

Such a list of ingredients can be judiciously combined with conventional fertilizer materials to make good full nutrition fertilizers at moderate costs. Such fertilizers would represent the first stage in moving toward sound food and ecological systems. It is worth noting that the three numerals on an ordinary fertilizer label designate the percentages of the total weight that are nitrogen, phosphate and potash, respectively. Most state fertilizer laws are still inadequate in providing for a sound formulation, labelling and sale of organic and full nutrition fertilizers. Therefore, with the addition of the materials just listed, we would have an organic based full diet 5–10–10 fertilizer for farm and garden use, compared with a simplistic 5–10–10 that offers only nitrogen, phosphate and potash in the cheapest forms.

Earth Foods

FERTILIZER FORMULAS

An Organic Based Full Nutrition 5–10–10 Fertilizer (In pounds per ton)		A Simplistic Dead Level 5–10–10 Fertilizer (In pounds per ton)	
100 lbs.	Ureaform	625 lbs.	Ammophos 16-20
400 lbs.	Feather meal	325 lbs.	Superphosphate 20%
300 lbs.	Bone meal		
200 lbs.	Seaweed	335 lbs.	Muriate of potash
300 lbs.	Ammophos 11-48	715 lbs.	Sand or Slag
300 lbs.	Leached langbenite	2,000 lbs.	Total
260 lbs.	Sulphate of potash		
40 lbs.	Fritted trace elements		
100 lbs.	Compost		
2,000 lbs.	Total		

The slower acting full diet fertilizer, when used at the rate of 1,200 pounds per acre, would cost about $30 per acre more, at present high prices for organic and trace element materials. Even so, the use of such a complete and superior fertilizer would not raise the inherent costs of most fruits and vegetables over 3% or 4%. Such a fertilizer would guarantee an adequate mineral composition of food and feed crops. Although transitional, such a fertilizer would begin to create a solid foundation for the national diet, and would utilize large quantities of human and animal organic wastes as well.

THE WASTE RECYCLING CHALLENGE

Transitional fertilizers such as the one described above, would consume some animal and poultry wastes, but still fail to open the channels for moving millions of tons of feedlot and sewage wastes back into U.S. farming. It represents Stage 1 in the revision of guides and objectives. A second stage, served by new technologies and business arrangements, will be needed.

Many of America's able scientists have been working on this problem in recent years. These include a research group at the Boeing Company in Seattle, Washington, another at the Brookhaven National Laboratory on Long Island, one at the Tennessee Valley Authority research center, and still another under the leadership of the Rodale Press, served by its magazine *Compost Science*.

One of the most promising of these developments, that we will delineate here as a key illustration, is the one led by Dr. Jim O'Donnell, president of Orgonics, Inc., at Slatersville, Rhode Island. Dr. O'Donnell has been engaged in work to improve and tame agricultural nitrogen since 1954, when he assisted Dr. K. G. Clark of the USDA, and others, in the research on ureaform nitrogen.

Dr. O'Donnell's research and manufacturing operations in recent years have centered in the organiform process. This is a technology which treats sewage wastes, feedlot manures, poultry wastes, leather scraps, and many other classes of organic wastes with slow-acting nitrogen and converts them into valuable high analysis fertilizers. It is clearly a promising technology for use in developing a high volume movement of such wastes back into our farming system.

Recently, for example, the city of Winston-Salem, North Carolina, built a million dollar plant to process and dry sewage and other organic wastes for the agricultural and horticultural markets. It proved, however, that the new enterprise could not reach its market because the inherent value of the product was too low to warrant shipping costs.

The organiform process is now being installed to perform the final production operation. It will convert the organic materials into an attractive slow-acting pelleted fertilizer with a 16% nitrogen content. The entire range of other plant foods can be added in the process, or can be added later in a blending operation insofar as they are not already present in the organic materials. The market range for this ultramodern product is over 1,000 miles. It is suitable for many kinds of high value horticulture including the Florida citrus industry.

This new process and others like it may open the way for recycling millions of tons of animal and human wastes back into U.S. agriculture. Composting is not enough. Its role, in many situations, is to serve as the initial stage in preparing feedlot manures, poultry wastes and sewage sludge for organiform processing. The second stage operation can take it on the long ride back to the farm.

Sioux City, Iowa, America's heartland city on the Missouri River, will illustrate a setting for the kinds of large-scale improvements that can be made to move organic wastes back into agriculture. It has been a livestock marketplace for over half a century, where millions of animals are received, fed, slaughtered, processed and shipped to retail markets all over the country.

Due to the presence of this organic industry, Sioux City has one of the nation's larger manure piles: longer than a football field and high as a hill, and the sewer lines from the slaughterhouse area have often run red with blood into the Missouri River. It is an impressive example of unmanageable wastes, too costly to handle and too large to ignore.

The city's civic and business leaders have been working to improve the situation. They have reduced the flow of blood into the river, and they are curtailing the accumulations of manure. Their old-fashioned methods are inadequate, however, to cope with the problem. A multiple agency approach that converts the wastes into saleable products is needed, and a model is available.

Terra Chemicals, International is near the slaughterhouses on a spacious land area. It is an ultra modern fertilizer manufacturing company, with annual sales of over 30 million dollars, selling fertilizers to half of the nation's farming districts. It is capable of receiving and processing Sioux City's manure, blood and sewage wastes, and incorporating them into organic based fertilizers and feed materials. It is prepared, theoretically, to utilize the organiform or other processes to recycle these wastes back into U.S. agriculture. The business and financial incentives need to be provided, however, through a creative use of public and private resources. The Environmental Protection Agency should find ways to mobilize these resources and provide the business incentives.

It would then be possible for Sioux City's meat companies to load the manure, blood and other slaughter wastes onto barges and transport them to Terra Chemical's land for composting. The city's sewage sludge could be added to the Terra Chemical compost piles, carried over in pipe lines. Composting would reduce these diverse materials into an acceptable organic matrix for processing into a high analysis fertilizer, valuable enough to be shipped into the Eastern half of U.S. agriculture.

What would such a fertilizer cost? Its price would be just low enough for farmers to accept, compared to other fertilizers, most of which would be inferior to this one in producing high value crops. And the price would be high enough to interest Terra Chemicals, International in conducting the enterprise. Other income would be generated

Earth Foods

from the meat companies, the city, and the Environmental Protection Agency. A composite drive by all these organizations and companies is essential to achieve large scale recycling of municipal and industrial wastes.

The other question is: What will it cost to fail in solving Sioux City's waste disposal problem?

In discussing the dimensions of this challenge to our farming system, Dr. T. C. Byerly, leader for USDA's waste disposal programs and its representative in the Environmental Protection Agency, says:[3]

". . . the total amount of waste produced by large-scale livestock operations is approximately equal to that produced by the entire population of the United States (estimated at 204 million in January 1970). By 1980, I estimate that the quantity of animal wastes subject to mass disposal methods will be double what it is today."

Table 1. Waste Disposal Problem For U.S. Livestock Raised In Large-Scale Operations In Terms Of Human Waste Equivalents

The amount of animal waste produced by—	Is equivalent to the human waste produced by—
5 million feedlot cattle	50 million people
7 million milk cows	105 million people
100 million laying hens	10 million people
50 million turkeys	5 million people
400 million broilers	20 million people
10 million hogs	10 million people
2 million lambs on feed	1 million people
Total equivalent	201 million people

He is saying, of course, that the mountain of animal and

[3] Byerly, T. C. "The Environment and Agriculture—Issues and Answers." *Agricultural Science Review* 8 (1970). Washington, D.C.: United States Department of Agriculture.

bird manure in America has finally grown until it is as high as the mountain of human manure. Both are still growing.

DDT was synthesized in 1874, and its ability to kill insects was discovered by Swiss scientists in 1939. Winston Churchill called it "the excellent DDT powder" in 1944. Rachel Carson named it "the elixir of death" in 1962. Today, every American eats one-tenth part per million of DDT in each pound of his food, and his body fat contains from 4 to 10 parts per million of the noxious stuff.[4]

Our planet is infected in its most remote places with the mother material of DDT, the chlorinated hydrocarbon chemical compounds. Antarctic fish and penguins have traces. Every acre of farm land in England has received more DDT in rainfall from air currents from the U.S. than the English farmers have applied to protect their crops.[5]

It is no longer possible in our country honestly to certify any food as free of DDT, because all of our food contains some of it. The question now is, how much is in the specific food product, an apple or a quart of milk, for example, and what amount is tolerable?

The USDA and FDA are still on the fence about DDT and related pesticides, due to intense lobbying by the chemical industry. These materials are not yet banned, as they should be. One facet of the problem is a lack of alternative crop protection materials that can take the place of

[4] Ottobone, Alice. Toxicologist, Food and Drug Laboratory, California State Department of Public Health. "DDT." From hearings before the House Agriculture Committee on the Federal Pesticide Control Act of 1971. U.S. Government Printing Office.

[5] Graham, Dr. Frank, Jr. *Since Silent Spring*. Boston: Houghton Mifflin, 1970.

those now in use. Here are two alternatives we should consider and use in a good food system.

SEAWEED TO PROTECT CROPS

The fertilizing powers of seaweed are well known. They have been celebrated by English and Channel Island farmers since 1694. The world production of seaweed for fertilizer and feed markets is now in excess of 500,000 metric tons, with Japan, Norway and Korea being leading producers.

That seaweed has a use in protecting crops is not so well known, however, and a vigorous research action is needed in the U.S. to assess this possible use.

According to the European and U.S. evidence, this interesting and unexplored material is capable of reducing many insect and virus populations, in fields normally infested, to a low enough level so significant crop damage does not occur. The dry granular form of seaweed can be used at the rate of from 200 to 300 pounds per acre as a fertilizer, to be ingested through the plant's roots. Plants or trees can also be sprayed two or three times during the season with a wettable or colloidal form of seaweed at the rate of about 12 ounces per acre application.

USDA research has been lagging in its attention to the possible insecticide properties of seaweed. The only sustained studies have been by Dr. T. L. Senn at Clemson University, supported for six years by the National Science Foundation. This work supports the premise that seaweed is effective both as a fertilizer and as an insect and disease repellent. A capable Midwest vegetable grower, Glenn Graber at Hartville, Ohio, is one of the leading supporters of the use of seaweed. His experience was described in testimony by Sheldon Z. Kaplan of the Sea-

Born Corporation, before the House Committee On Agriculture on the Federal Pesticide Control Act of 1971. He quoted the *Cleveland Plain Dealer* for July 21, 1963:

By using a seaweed product, a muckland farmer has produced more than 100,000 packages of vegetables so far this year without using one pound of insecticide.

Glenn J. Graber, owner of a 600-acre blackdirt truck farm, gives the thanks to a liquid and meal product made from Norwegian seaweed.

His farm was the first in this area and possibly in Ohio to give the product extensive use.

The seaweed used is nontoxic and is of the floating variety. Norway has Europe's biggest seaweed resources, estimated at over 10 million tons.

Graber is so satisfied with the results that he says that 'we eventually hope to raise our produce entirely without insecticides.

'With this seaweed product, I never hesitate to eat a raw plant, even while walking through a field on my farm.

'I've found that in the first year of use you do not see the drastic results that come in the next few years. And the use of this product has cut in half my cost of insect control,' he said.

'Generally,' Graber said, 'the seaweed product gives plants more resistance to disease and insects, longer shelf life and produces a more healthy plant.

'We couldn't tell too much last spring about the cold,' said Graber, 'but last fall we harvested spinach until December 5 when the snow came, and radishes until November 5. Usually we had to quit before by the middle of October.

'While I have no connection with the promotion or sale of the product, I feel it eventually will be widely used in the United States.'

The authors know Glenn Graber, and can testify to his competence as a vegetable farmer with over 20 years of experience. He produces about 600 acres of diversified vegetables a year.

71

MIXED FARMING VERSUS MONOCULTURES

There has been no hindrance in the past 30 years to the unhealthy concentration of crop, animal and bird production. The public subsidies in agriculture have actually hastened the trend toward giant enterprise units—called monocultures—in corn, chickens, vegetables, beef feed lots, hogs, apples, potatoes and other food crops. The trend has been not only to large unit sizes, but also to massive concentrations in communities, areas and regions.

Arkansas, for example, now produces over 400 million poultry broilers a year, not counting turkeys and egg laying hens. These huge flocks produce nearly 2 million tons of manure annually, plus feathers and slaughter wastes, and are now leading causes of land and water pollution.

These monocultures, large operations in one single crop or enterprise, are also massive incubators for every pest, insect and disease known. The poultry, for example, have to be drugged, doped and inoculated until they are little walking drug stores, to prevent epidemics from sweeping through their colonies. The corn, hog, vegetable and beef monocultures, miles long in a single community, are similar insect and disease breeders.

The USDA pays farmers over $3.5 billion a year under the banner of supporting a good system of farming. This is not, however, a good system, and public payments are helping it to get worse by accelerating automation and encouraging monocultures.

An overhauled USDA, rephased in its research directives, should give attention to investing the public's money in new sectors of research and development which would answer the question: What are alternative pesticides and ways of protecting crops, that are safe for people and the environment? Is the use of seaweed a solution? How can mixed farming, instead of monocultures, be encouraged with the investments of public funds?

People who live in cities used to love to visit the country, because once they came there and perhaps their Aunt Nellie still lived there. Walking in fields of grain and seeing the cows and chickens was a refreshing experience. Eating bread and milk and fried chicken topped the little holiday.

Now it is barren. You can drive a hundred miles without finding a diversified farm, much less Aunt Nellie or some cows and chickens. The city folk have no country cousins anymore. They go to the mountains or seashore, instead, to camp among the dense colonies there.

In this chapter, we could have offered a diagram of an ideal farm, using the principles we have delineated. Instead, we have outlined farming materials and patterns that may help to overcome America's food dilemma and its attendant dolorous pollution problems.

There are three main thoughts: 1) We do have many of the techniques and materials for a safe, sound and low cost production of food crops and animals. The prospects, in this respect, are encouraging; 2) Our main necessity, nationally, is a redirection of farm policies and an overhauling of the use of farm subsidy and research funds, so they effectively support good food production and large volume recycling of organic wastes; 3) A great leap forward from the present distorted monoculture farming pattern is imperative into modern organic farming or a decentralized social and economic system. This is too much to expect, as a rapid development. The big cities and the big manure piles will still be with us for a while, for quite a while.

A good immediate objective is a vigorous transition

that begins to set up quality food production and marketing units to serve interested urban customers, still within our faulty system. The Earth Food guides are adequate for such transitional developments.

We must demand integrity in the U.S. food system during the 1970's but we cannot afford purism.

CHAPTER FIVE

The Gustatory Values of Foods

TRULY, MAN DOES not live by bread alone, nor only by the gut values of his foods. It is the whole experience of eating that fills him deeply, emotionally as well as physically: aromas, special flavors, feelings of companionship, security, freedom from want, the warmth of the family group, of a dash of pepper, of a cup of wine, of saving the tid-bits for the dog or cat. These are all part of the satisfactions of eating good foods.

When our nation built its highway system and then its airlines, radio and TV networks, it put together the biggest and richest market system in the world. Previously, neighborhoods and communities had many individual tastes, and you had a "home area" in your eating preferences. These were based on strong flavors—your special home breads, venison, stew, borscht, beer, chitlins, cheese or sauerkraut, and on your kinship with the hearty foods of working people.

As the big market was put together, the food industry levelled off the glorious tastes and differences, and made most foods bland and tasteless. This, along with incessant advertising, enabled the industry to get acceptance of food items over the whole market, with a minimum of different

75

recipes and packages. They removed some of the finest flavor factors in order to get shelf life for the products. By taking the wheat germs out of bread, they also took out proteins and minerals. The United States, as a net result of these product changes, now has one of the blandest, most boring, dead-level food supplies in the whole world.

Luckily, you cannot consider rebuilding a sound and nutritious food system without also reinstating these precious gustatory values of foods, since good nutrition and excellent flavor often go hand in hand. But logic almost ends there. It is also true that flavor and palatability in foods are individual matters. Nothing is more deeply personal and psychologically conditioned, than a person's relations with his daily foods, and his favorite foods. Once the conditioning has occurred, there is no assurance that the foods a person likes will be good for him. The people of West Africa, for example, love cassava although it is 98% starch and would make white rats climb walls looking for something to eat.

Your personal acceptance of a particular dish or kind of food may be illogical and baffling to other people. If this seems unlikely, try eating

- The eyeballs of a caribou or the warm stomach contents of a walrus, recently killed, unless you are an Eskimo.
- Fried squash blossoms, unless you are a Filipino.
- Boiled cow anuses, unless you are an Angi tribesman of West Africa.
- Boiled chicken heads, unless you are a Malaysian.
- Fat worms, unless you live in Kenya.
- Raw fish and seaweed, unless you are Japanese.

· Chitlins, unless you were raised in Georgia, the Carolinas, or thereabouts.

· Hamburgers, unless you are an American.

What are your soul foods? We have searched for the great foods of our own lives and communities, and have discovered striking differences, even though we came from similar generations of Western Americans.

Lee's early food was bread and milk, slurpy bread and milk. Within each bowl of it there were differences between the soaked pieces in the bottom and the half-dunked ones on top. You stirred until it was just right. The bread was home made, and the milk was creamy, no "blue john," as the Western settlers contemptuously called skim milk.

Akin to the bread and milk was a simple variation that had no name. It was this: Lee would be out hunting squirrels or plowing a nearby field when the agonies of hunger would overtake him. He'd race to the house, cut a big piece of bread, rush to the milk shelves, slap the bread on top of a creamy pan of milk, rush to the sugar bin, slap the dripping bread into the sugar, and rush back to the hunting or plowing.

Now consider this: If the cream was just right, about 5 hours old, it seeped richly into the bread and the sugar and tasted near to heaven. Was this a good food? Was the subject even debatable at that place and time? But also consider this: the cows on Lee's farm probably had *brucellosis*, Bang's disease or contagious abortion, which can infect humans. Also, those pans of milk always had one-fourth of an inch of grey-brown sediment in the bottom, so it was a family practice to throw that part out. The sediment, of course, was the dust and manure that fell into the pails when the cows were being milked, more in the winter when the cows were confined and less in the summer when they grazed in the pastures.

A question: Which would be the better and safer milk? That milk, or the semi-embalmed milk of today, with its additives and little cargoes of DDT?

The four small islands of muscle meat on the back of a fried chicken, and the meat of the neck, were also among Lee's soul foods, gone today since the birds are ill-fed and the bone meat spoils with storage. Pan gravy was also included, two kinds to use on bread or potatoes: the first made with flour and milk from the grease and crumbs of fried meats, evil and brown from sautéeing the flour, and the second made with thickening and milk from the grease and goo of roasted meats.

Potatoes and gravy, bread and gravy, were so delicious that they upstaged cake and pie. A dessert was just more food.

Lee has other food memories, but these will illustrate a person's strong psychological attachments to family foods.

Dick, the epicurean even in childhood, hated bread and milk, and was cool to potatoes and gravy. His taste for acid-sweetness prevailed at an early age. He savored Malt-O-Meal for its sweet taste combined with chocolate bitterness. Meat and vegetables were eaten mainly so he could get at the pie—lemon and chocolate in winter and apple, cherry or berry in the summer—again the sweet-sour foods.

As a food chemist and menu maker during World War II, Dick noted that prisoners of war got morale and a taste lift from putting sugar on their beans, the sweet-sour thing, again. This was an old custom among black families of the South.

If Dick, the gourmet cook, were to prepare his favorite dish of today, it probably would be a Spanish spiced stew made of meat, onions, garbanzo beans, tomatoes, hot peppers and wine, balancing the sweet from the vegetables and the sour from the wine, braced with the peppers. He also loves leek and potato soup savored with a bit of lemon juice. Bouillabaisse, a special fish chowder, is a delight to him.

The finest entree when friends come, however, is a poached fish in court bouillon, with vegetable seasoning and a bit of wine added. The fish is served with a sauce that is built from the bouillon stock, with gentle but piquant seasoning.

WE NEED A NATIONAL FOOD

Dick Gregory, one of America's advanced students of foods and people, said, "A major problem in this country is that we have no national food, no low cost food that is generally eaten and enjoyed by everyone, that even a poor man can bring home and feel glad, because he has fed his family again."

Think of it a minute. The national and folk groupings of the world, in their great years, have had widely accepted low cost foods, such as: Rice for the billions of people in the rice-eating countries, foo foo and other main meal dishes made from cassava, plantain and pounded yams in Africa, fish stews with rice in island cultures, beans in Mexico and Latin America, greens and spare parts of pork in Southern and black communities, country bread, wine and beer in European countries.

What can we say about America? To be honest about it, we have to say that our national foods are tasteless white bread, credit card steaks, hamburgers, milk shakes, french fries and potato chips. Even the regional gourmet dishes, such as Chinook salmon, Dungeness and Chesapeake crabs, razor clams, Cape Cod lobster, Creole fish stew, corn fed beef steaks and southern fried chicken are going with the winds and the pollution of our foods and waters. What can a working man bring home today for $1, from which to make a nutritious family meal, feeding them in mind and spirit as well as body?

It is a problem. We have no nutritious, low cost national food.

As we, in America, rise above our bestial needs, toward sufficiency, and then to plenty, should not our interests turn to the gustatory values of eating as well as to feeding our bodies? Can we restore these precious soul values of foods, without turning back our technical and economic clocks and going to our dinners in Model T Fords?

Of course we can. An Arkansas or Georgia broiler chicken is only a grotesque shadow of the wild barnyard fowl we used to love for Sunday dinner. That long-legged bird ate seeds, weeds, clover, grasses, bugs, grain, rocks and milk, and out of the melange he built nutritious and tasty drumsticks, breast meat, wings n' things. And the eggs laid by his mate were formed from the same diversified feeds.

Is this so mysterious and complex an undertaking that we cannot duplicate those same nutritional and flavor values with modern menu planning for chickens? We think not. It is simply a challenge to be undertaken with confidence, since we possess the food sciences and the arts for producing almost any known food to specifications.

The main hazard is in failing to budget enough arts and skills for getting good low cost foods accepted and eaten in the local neighborhoods. It is in getting overstaffed with food scientists and dieticians who fail to know how people tick and not employing enough good psychologists. It is in the fact again that food tastes and acceptance are basically illogical, and are the end results of personal experiences. Let us illustrate this, all over again, because it is so very important, with two small vignettes: (1) In Alaska, for many years, the only eggs available were "boat eggs" —ones that had made the long trip on the boat from Seattle to Anchorage or Fairbanks. The supplies changed, however, with expansion, and it was then possible to get, also, (a) airplane eggs—flown in overnight, and (b) fresh local eggs from such places as the Mananuska Valley. Did Alaskans readily choose the new fresh eggs, and jump for joy? No. They were used to "boat eggs" and the others tasted strange. "Boat eggs" had become Alaskan soul food. Many old time Alaskans never could fully accept and enjoy "fresh eggs."

And (2) . . . For many, many years, the caps of beer bottles were lined with cork, neatly glued in place. Bye and bye, as the markets expanded, the cork supplies ran low and were undependable. The beer companies had to shift to plastic, for lining their bottle caps. What happened? They got hundreds of complaints because "the beer companies were tampering with the flavor of the beer." All they were doing, really, was removing the cork flavor.

America has produced a generation of young people for whom soul food is a chintzy hamburger, a soda and an envelope of french fries. The biggest error would be to assume that such a food pattern would be changed by logic or coercion. Voluntary change by these young eaters, in response to valid incentives, will have to occur. Or, a change that is so subtle that it is hardly noticed, such as: Putting 15% protein in bigger, fatter, jucier hamburgers, via adding good soy meal or other vegetable materials. Improving the buns with similar supplements, using ad-

81

vanced food skills to disguise the blessed additives. Restoring some milk to the milk shakes.

A new trend, however, is seen. It is in the food studies and selections of a still newer generation of young Americans who are getting wise to the flim-flam and dishonesty of our business system. They don't believe the advertising anymore. They are hunting for sensible life styles. They are rejecting the multi-layers of bags and packaging with their gorgeous labels, and demanding cheap and basic foods once more. We predict they will get basic foods, and that sitting in franchised chicken palaces and hamburger emporiums will get to be a very "out" thing to do. Those who are burning their draft cards and raising hell on the campuses may be running our food industry 30 years from now. If so, some of us old timers may have a hard time getting enough polysaturated fats to keep us happy.

Money

Once there was an island of beautiful intelligent people,
named the Sealanders, who learned to carve woods,
weave clothing and build villages. The chief and
the witch doctor guided their lives.

These people used stones for money. This helped with
their trade and measured their labor and wealth.

The people who finally acquired large stones were
very wealthy, and they were privileged to carve their
names on them to signify their ownership, and wealth.

It happened that the richest family on the island, with
the largest stone, decided to move across the lagoon,
where they had planted new coconut trees.

They carried their big stone in a large canoe, but alas,
the canoe overturned and the big stone sank to the
bottom of the lagoon.

This did not disturb the economy of the island, or the
wealth of this family, because everyone knew they

owned that stone, bearing their name, as it lay at the bottom of the lagoon.

Then, bad news! Catastrophe!

The enemy Atolians invaded the island, and their Man Flint knew about the Sealander's money system. He dived in the lagoon, and leered as he cut off that noble family's name and wrote ATOL.

He also wrote ATOL on all of the big rocks of this lovely island, destroying its wealth, rock by rock.

Then the Atolians departed, but what a tragedy!

The Sealanders were bankrupt. Their economy was destroyed. The Atolians had taken their wealth. They had lost their rocks.

CHAPTER SIX ♪

Financial and
Business Arrangements

THE FINANCIAL situation in the U.S. is not quite as absurd as the one just described, of the Sealanders who lost their rocks and their wealth. We are, however, wedded to some impractical customs in business and government which we will have to revise if we are to survive as a strong people on our planet. Their man Flint may sneak in and bankrupt us if we cannot learn how to finance our life-and-death food and anti-pollution enterprises.

These business fields, foods and anti-pollution, defy old-fashioned concepts of feasibility. They do not lend themselves to short-range styles of financing and business analysis. Community interest simply has to be expressed as a business force, lest we poison our foods and drinking water and suffocate in our own gasses and sewage.

The U.S. business world resembles our solar system, our sun, moon and stars, in the way it has developed by making big units from smaller ones. In the case of the solar system, the astronomers tell us, it started with clouds of small bits of matter, some of them gaseous. Then, the forces of the universe caused the larger bits of matter to attract the smaller ones, and begin moving in circular pathways. They inevitably bumped into one another, however, and got into each other's fields of force, as they sped around through space. The small ones captured the tiny ones, the big ones got the small ones, the giant ones got the big ones, and the stubborn ones, that just wouldn't give up, became moons. They were held by the gravity of the big planets and could not get away. They will circle forever.

In the case of the U.S. business system, the auto industry is a good illustration of the process of making big ones out of little ones. Think of it: Dart, Dodge, Star, Chevrolet, Moon, Pierce Arrow, Auburn, Cord, Durant, Winton, Apperson, Stutz, Marmon, Stanley, Overland, Buick, Frazier, Franklin, Willys, Paige, Graham, Kaiser, White, Nash, and a score of others . . . all to make our three giants. Not even Packard and Studebaker could survive.

The same business forces that reduced the auto industry to a barren plain of non-competition have been at work in farming and food production. Let us examine these forces, using the poultry enterprise as a convenient illustration.

Nearly all of the earlier farmers had chickens. A hundred hens would give enough eggs for the family and the hired help and enough birds for chicken dinners. The surplus was sold to local stores and produce buyers. Then, many medium-sized and part time poultrymen all over the country raised eggs and chickens for the city markets. In 1939, 2,519,000 farmers sold chickens. A 50,000 flock was a large one. Many a farm wife was selling eggs and chickens to dress her family and keep one or more children in school.

There was no broiler industry in 1940, to produce young chicken meat in factory style for the supermarket trade. Poultry broilers incidentally are young chickens produced for meat, sometimes called fryers. They are produced in confinement on high energy feeds in from 8 to 10 weeks, and sold at about a 4 pound weight.

The feed companies and the city produce operators moved in on this situation between 1945 and 1955. A hypothetical case would be that of a company, Poultry Unlimited, in a particular trade area, put together by a big local feed company, backed by a national feed company, and serving the rising supermarket demands for bargain meats. Poultry Unlimited did not actually keep or produce the birds. It made contracts for their production with many local farmers that were in a budget squeeze. The production contracts were deadly, at prices that often allowed less than 50¢ an hour for the farmer's labor and management. It was eventually said that a family could not afford to enter into one of these contracts unless they were on social security or they would starve to death.

Then the wheels turned, crunch, crunch, crunch, and Poultry Unlimited got into its own budget squeeze. It was bought by a competitor, who got bought by a larger one. The big feed companies smelled trouble and ran for cover, selling their interests to the smart new operators, but still supplying the trainloads of feed at bargain prices.

An integration of the broiler enterprise was then effected, based upon a consolidation of financing, feed supply, technical services, production, dressing, processing and marketing, all under one umbrella in a community or a region.

The accumulated impact of these changes, knocking out the small producers and integrating the rest of them, hit the country between 1955 and 1960. The farm price for the young broilers was 25¢ a pound, live weight, in 1955, still at its 1945-55 level. By 1965, it was 15¢ a pound, where it is today. The wholesale price of chicken dropped 40% even during this inflationary period.

Most of America's chickens are now produced by about 6,000 operators. The production is concentrated in 10 states which account for 84% of it.[6]

	Number
State	*Produced In 1969*
Georgia	442 million
Arkansas	415 million
Alabama	353 million
North Carolina	281 million
Mississippi	221 million
Maryland	174 million
Texas	171 million
Delaware	134 million
California	77 million
Maine	73 million
Total	2.339 billion

Some would suggest that it is time, now, to salute the flag and clap our hands because of this stunning reduction in the price of chicken in the supermarkets, achieved through U.S. business genius. Let us, instead, look at the hole we have dug for ourselves, not counting the wear and tear on a million ex-farm housewives who used to get extra mad money from their flocks of hens.

THE QUALITY OF THE MEAT

Chickens, let us remember, used to be able to walk and fly. They were not jailbirds. They took their time in growing their bones and muscles. Even during the thirties when poultry raising was quite advanced, a farmer budgeted

[6] Unpublished data from the Poultry Group, Economic Research Service, U.S. Department of Agriculture. 1971.

four pounds of feed for each pound of gain in the chickens he was feeding for market. Outdoor pasture was recommended for laying hens.

Today, however, the broilers are being produced with about two pounds of feed per pound of gain in the birds. Arsenic, antibiotics and pharmaceuticals are often added to their feed to help them achieve a fantastic rate of growth, and to prevent epidemics of diseases and parasites among the colonies of confined birds. The USDA *Agriculture Handbook No. 320, Commercial Broiler Production*,[7] says that as a general guide, 3.15% of the direct costs of producing these young chickens should be budgeted for medication and vaccination, not counting the growth stimulants. The following additives are sufficiently common to be topically listed. The quotations are exactly as they appear in this USDA guide.

Antibiotics.
Most broiler rations contain antibiotics at the relatively low levels of 4 to 10 grams per ton to stimulate growth. Some of those commonly used are penicillin, bacitracin, zinc bactiracin, erythromycin, chlortetracycline, and oxytetracycline. Improved results are sometimes obtained by combining antibiotics or by changing antibiotics periodically.

Arsenicals.
Low levels of certain arsenicals have a growth effect similar to that of antibiotics. Arsenicals and antibiotics usually have a greater growth response when combined than when used separately. For example, the addition of arsanilic acid or "3-nitro" to bacitracin methylene disalicylate will give a better gain and feed conversion than the antibiotics alone. The pigmentation of the birds fed on arsenicals is often improved. . . .

[7] *Commercial Broiler Production.* (Agriculture Handbook No. 320. Agricultural Research Service. U.S. Department of Agriculture. U.S. Government Printing Office. 1967.)

Hormones.

Dienestrol diacetate, a synthetic compound with hormone-like activity, has been mixed with feed to increase fat deposition and to give improved carcass quality. When any product of this kind is used, the manufacturer's directions and the Food and Drug Administration's regulations should be followed.

Xanthophyll.

In most areas, customers prefer highly pigmented birds. The variation in skin color is due primarily to breed, method of scald, and the xanthophylls in the feed ingredients of the rations. Xanthophylls are a group of carotenoid pigments. Good pigmentation usually results when at least 6.4 mg. of xanthophyll from natural sources are present in each pound of feed. If low carotenoid ingredients, such as milo or white corn, are used in a starter ration, good pigmentation can still be obtained by using about 8 mg. of xanthophyll per pound of finisher ration. . . .

Miscellaneous Additives.

Some of the miscellaneous additives used in broiler rations and their functions are as follows:

ADDITIVE	FUNCTION
Aterrimin	Growth stimulant.
Dynafac	Growth promotion and feed conversion.
Furazolidone, nf-180	Chemotherapeutic agent for growth promotion and prevention and treatment of fowl typhoid, paratyphoid, pullorum disease, and CRD.
Neomycin, neomycin sulfate	Used for bacterial enteritis.
Nystatin, Mycostatin	For prevention and treatment of crop mycosis and mycotic diarrhea.
Reserpine	To combat stress conditions.
Sulfathiazole sodium	To control spread of infectious coryza.

An indicator of the malnutrition of these chickens is

the poor calcification of their bones, which are grown too fast to develop properly. If you examine their bones, you will notice a bluish color, and often small blood vessels in them will be visible. The forced growth rate is also too fast to permit the formation of much fat.

Are these birds fit for human consumption, and are they acceptable as America's low cost source of meat protein?

Frankly, no one knows how to answer that question. USDA is not doing much research on the quality of foods as influenced by the methods of production, as we noted previously in discussing carrots. The flavor of the broilers is deplorable, however, due to malnutrition of the birds, and the food safety situation is very unsatisfactory, at least in part because one episode of contamination can affect millions of chickens and people.

In an incident reported as "Millions Of Chickens Tainted" in *The Washington Post* on July 29, 1971, such an epidemic contamination occurred. At a feed plant in North Carolina, PCB, a DDT-like material, leaked into the feed. This one source, due to the concentration of the poultry industry, produced feed for 35 million birds a week. The industry, as is chronically the case, did not have adequate quality and safety controls, so the contamination went undetected, and the poisoned birds went into the supermarkets of a whole marketing region.

The enormity of it all overwhelmed USDA so that the agency was afraid to act. It hushed up the event for a week or more so the public could consume the poisoned birds and get them off the market.

The public, the USDA spokesman said, "should not be unduly alarmed. It is not worthwhile to worry the consumer now about something he ate a few weeks ago. It hasn't affected my consumption of chicken. As far as we know every chicken sitting on every shelf is safe and wholesome."

Rep. William Fitts Ryan (D-N.Y.) had a different view. He filed a bill to prohibit all production or use of PCB in the U.S. and said he was shocked and outraged by the government's handling of the case. "They're just playing guessing games," he said. "The setting of the 5 parts per million standard was purely arbitrary in the first place. From all we can find the action of Agriculture and the FDA has been insufficient to say the least. They've hushed up earlier PCB contamination cases and delayed the announcement in this case until the chickens had been sold. This is unconscionable neglect in a situation of staggering potential harm."

PCB has not been studied sufficiently by the Food and Drug Administration, USDA or other research agencies so its effects on humans are unknown. It has been shown, however, to cause low fertility in fowl and liver damage in rats. Some scientists think it may pose a long term peril to animals and people. In the case of the leakage into the chicken feed, reported above, the problem was traced only after one of the plant's feed customers found that his chickens were getting sick and becoming sterile. Still USDA could say, after millions of innocent consumers had eaten the tainted chickens that they "should not be unduly alarmed."

Clearly, the unit size, concentration, production technologies, incentives and controls in the U.S. poultry enterprises are inadequate to assure the safety and quality of the poultry products. Improvements in this sector of the food industry are needed. Forty years ago a food poisoning episode was always local. Today, it may sicken 10 million people. The mode of production, itself, is debasing the safety and quality of this food.

POLLUTION OF LAND AND WATER

We talked recently with an influential public official, who has the power to grant or deny resources for use in farming developments. He was totally unaware that poultry and livestock manure and slaughter wastes have become public liabilities and large scale pollution hazards. He still thought that manure was a homey resource for farming.

The facts are different. Dr. L. H. Hileman, Agronomist at the University of Arkansas, dealt with this subject in a paper he presented to the Agricultural Waste Conference at Cornell University in February of 1970. He said:[8]

> Continuous heavy (10 tons or more per acre) applications of broiler house poultry litter-manure has had and is causing a drastic unbalance in the soil's chemical content. Soil chemical unbalance has resulted in partial sterility of the soil for crop production; impounded water contamination; underground water contamination; and deficient and toxic forage for livestock.
>
> Some form of mechanical or biological processing seems to be the only presently feasible method of eliminating contamination. Composting has been most successful in Arkansas. The process is expensive and the resulting product costs more to make than its value in terms of fertilizer elements.

Hileman, in a letter to the authors dated March 2, 1970, supplemented his paper given at the Agricultural Waste Management with the following statement:

> Needless to say, the situation here in Arkansas has not improved since your correspondence. We still have the

[8] Hileman, L. H. Agronomist. *Pollution Factors Associated with Excessive Litter (Manure) Applications in Arkansas*. University of Arkansas, 1970.

problem with poultry manure waste and it would appear that even more problems are arising from the disposal of the solids from sewage treatment plants. . . . Just as alarming is the fact that most of these plants are located near a flowing stream and the erosion and effluent find their way into this stream, polluting it for many miles. The Arkansas Pollution Commission recently completed a study of the Dardanelle Basin on the Arkansas River. Over one half of the commercial plants (poultry) and the sewage treatment plants were not meeting minimum specifications for dumping their materials into contributory streams.

Dr. Hileman's findings can be duplicated in all leading poultry producing states. This is due to the fact that the business arrangements, financial incentives, and public services in this industry are inadequate to protect land, water, livestock and people.

LESSONS FROM THE U.S. POULTRY ENTERPRISE

The example of the U.S. poultry enterprise is useful in designing financial and business arrangements for improving our food supply system. It offers lessons that bear careful thought, for example: The price structure for a food product can be pitched at a high, medium or low level, and, in a sense, the net effects are civic and social. The 1955 poultry price of 25¢ gave better quality chickens, safer supplies, employed more people, and caused no major pollution problems. The 15¢ price, on the other hand, is a sucker's price for everyone, consumers included. It is too low to enable the industry to cover all of its production costs, including the cost of producing well nourished birds, the cost of adequate testing and safety and quality controls, and the cost of processing and disposing of the wastes. Clearly, in our present day and age of rising taxes and public cost, the resources for improving this enterprise must come mainly from private sources, rather than from federal or state funds. They have to be derived from retail dollars out of a controlled revision in the retail and wholesale prices for poultry products.

THE ROLES OF GOVERNMENT AND CONSUMERS

The role of government is to represent consumers as well as producers in seeing that the industry faces its internal problems in safety, quality and waste disposal. It can provide a pattern for the industry to relate to in making the essential improvements, which necessarily will include a revision in prices. Then, it can provide turn around loans, grants and services to assist the industry in getting back to a sound production, pricing, marketing and waste disposal basis.

Consumers must use their buying power to support the retailers and producers that help to clean up this debased enterprise by buying good chickens that are produced under approved conditions. Their further role is civic-political, to compel government food agencies and the industry to serve, in fact, the public interest.

AN EXAMPLE OF ESSENTIAL PRICE CHANGES

Let us use a poultry broiler enterprise that produces 300,000 birds annually as an example in revising prices so they will cover all of the costs of producing a good and safe product, and disposing of the wastes. Let us call this the Rosebud Poultry Company.

Here are the assumptions: The present farm price for live birds is 15¢ a pound. The present production costs are 12½¢ a pound, so the gross profit based on selling price is a modest 16.7%. A competent study shows that cutting out the questionable feed additives and restoring a fairly well balanced diet for the birds will increase the feed requirements so it takes 3 pounds of feed rather than 2 pounds to produce a pound of gain in the birds. This change in feed requirement, with the feed at $80 per ton, will cost 4¢ per pound of meat, or 16¢ per bird assuming that any additional costs for hauling, labor, etc. will be offset by reductions in additives, veterinary costs and losses of birds. Another study shows that the net costs of processing and disposing of the wastes (during a development in this phase) will amount to ½¢ per pound, or 2¢ per bird.

If these assumptions are made, the Rosebud Company would have to increase the price of its broilers to 19½¢ per pound in order to furnish good quality birds and recycle the wastes.

This increase of 4½¢ a pound, carried in the retail price, would amount to a 6¢ per pound increase in the price for the dressed birds on the supermarket counter. Reasons for the narrow spread between the farm price increase and the retail price increase are: The costs of dressing, packing, and hauling the birds are already covered. Only distributing and retailing cost margins need be added, and the supermarket margins on broilers are very low, often in the range of 12% to 15%.

We suggest, based upon such an assessment, that consumers, members of the poultry industry, and public officials should begin to think of these cost and price increases, when considering an improvement in the poultry enterprise, in order to offer better choices to quality and safety minded customers.

The example of the Rosebud Poultry Company enables us to relate to three alternatives of food supply that consumers should be privileged to support with their purchases at their favorite markets. (1) The organic and natural food alternative, illustrated by organic chickens that are raised on organic feeds and good pasture. They will be expensive, perhaps 90¢ a pound. (2) The factory production alternative, illustrated by present day supplies of broilers, but improved so safety of the product can be reasonably well assured (cut down on the growth stimulants and pharmaceuticals and get safety controls), and so the wastes are disposed of. They will be low in price, perhaps 37¢ a pound. (3) A certified good quality alternative, illustrated by well grown chickens, raised on 3¼ to 1 ratio of feed to gain in weight, and with a built-in waste disposal allowance. They will have a medium price, perhaps 43¢ a pound.

Our attention can be focused on how to get such produce into the markets, in response to consumer demands for better, safer foods and a range of choices. How can this be done from a practical financial and business standpoint?

PRODUCTION CONTRACTS FOR BETTER FOODS

The food industry has used production contracts to get the crops it needs, grown according to specifications, for years. Food and Earth Services, Inc. has in fact assisted in preparing such contracts, and has assisted growers in producing for them. We assisted the Nalley Company of Tacoma, Washington, in getting the quality of potatoes it wanted for making potato chips. We assisted the pea growers of Skagit Valley, Washington in producing tender peas for their Stokeley Van Camp contracts. Such production arrangements offer incentives to the growers for adequately fertilizing their crops and harvesting them carefully, in order to enjoy an assured market, and higher prices and profits.

A typical contract would say, in effect,

(1) I, John Doe, the grower, hereby agree to produce 100 acres of "X" crops for the Sunset Food Company, and agree to produce it in the following manner, . . .
(2) The Sunset Food Company, in turn, agrees to purchase the crop at "Y" prices for grades specified as follows, . . . (3) The crop will be inspected and tested in such and such a manner, to assure that it is acceptable and that John Doe has grown it in a careful manner, in accordance with this agreement, . . .
(4) The Sunset Food Company, in order to facilitate the production, agrees to provide six thousand dollars in operating funds to assist John Doe in this production, and it also agrees to provide technical counselling and assistance through its fieldmen.

It is only one short step to adapt such a contract and business agreement for the mutually controlled production of honest organic products and high quality, safe, laboratory tested and certified food products whether they be poultry, oranges, tomatoes, carrots, lettuce, apples, potatoes, bananas, beef, milk, eggs, wheat, bread or any other basic food.

A well-run supermarket can make contracts for the production of well-fed broilers grown only at a place that processes its wastes. It can cater to its quality, safety and ecology-minded customers in the promotion of a profitable patronage and market. We would predict that half of the customers of many supermarkets would soon switch to this safe and flavorable merchandise, with added thousands after each bungling episode of the food industry and the public food agencies in trying to cover up their mistakes.

The production contracts, where poultry is concerned, can specify the feeding guides (such as 3½ pounds of feed per pound of gain), and have covenants prohibiting the use of objectionable feed additives. They can provide for competent laboratory analyses of samples of the feed and of the birds. The grower, supported by the laboratory, can certify the product, and the certification can be displayed by the retailers. A bond may thereby be established between the grower and the ultimate consumers.

In the case of carrots, oranges and other produce, the contracts can specify full nutrition fertilizers and they can limit the insecticides, herbicides and other crop protection procedures to those that are positively harmless both to people and to the environment in their long term effects. A competent laboratory, again, can take samples, assess the crop for quality and safety, and assist in certifying it if the analyses confirm predetermined quality and safety standards.

Such business arrangements, we suggest, are practical and essential to open up adequate supplies of truly acceptable food at reasonable prices for America's growing multitudes of quality-minded customers.

HOW TO CERTIFY FOODS FOR SAFETY AND QUALITY

A useful precedent for certifying foods as to safety and quality can be found in U.S. seed certification services. These services in the seed trades are similar to those we will surely need to restore safety and quality in basic food products.

A crop improvement association is the key organization that handles such a service to certify the quality of seeds. It sets the standards of purity and integrity for each particular kind of seed, and administers the testing and inspection program that assists growers in producing seed crops for discriminating markets. Such associations are private nonprofit organizations that are authorized by state laws. The Oregon Crop Improvement Association is an example of how such organizations perform their work.

The Oregon Association accepts for membership seed growers who wish to produce certified seed for quality seed markets. The growers pay an annual membership fee, as well as fees for the services they use. Seed cleaning plants and processors may also participate in the program, since their services are vital to producing and marketing the products. The seedmen of the state university and Department of Agriculture also have vital roles to perform, and they participate. The Board of Directors and officers of the Crop Improvement Association represent all these various groups that comprise Oregon's seed industry.

The seed crops are tested and certified for a number of crucial standards: Purity, or relative freedom from noxious weed seeds, other weeds, dirt, additives and adulteration; germination, or the percent of the seeds that will actually sprout and grow, and be useful to the customer; purity of variety, or whether the seed product is actually what it is represented as.

The insurance of these vital factors in a crop of seeds requires that several services be purchased from the Association by the growers. The kinds of services may vary with the different kinds of crops and seeds. Basic, however, are: making a field inspection of the crop while it is growing; getting the production history of the crop; taking samples of the seeds; making laboratory tests of these samples; and issuing reports and certifications.

The growers of certified Pennlawn grass seed, for example, will register their fields with the Crop Improvement Association, and request the certification services.

The Association will then schedule field inspections during the growing season. Qualified seedmen, often from the state university, are employed to visit the various farms. They examine the appearance of the crops, note the kinds and amounts of weeds in the fields, and check for plant diseases. They also obtain the production history of the land and determine the kind and quality of the seed that was planted for this reproduction. All of this information is in the Association's records for use in deciding later whether a certification of quality will be issued.

After the crop is harvested and cleaned, a representative sample of the seed is carefully taken and sent to the Association's laboratory for testing, and a report is issued. This document, plus the field inspection report, then serves as valid evidence of the purity, germination and varietal integrity of the seed crop. If it meets predetermined standards, the Association may certify the product as pure high quality Pennlawn grass seed, to be labelled as such wherever it is sold.

The costs of these seed testing and certification services are quite low, and are fully recovered in the enhancement of the value of the crop. The fees for field inspection of the crop may run about one dollar per acre, and the costs for laboratory services will be from ten dollars to twenty-five dollars per sample, depending on the kind of seed. In seeds, as in foods, these essential production costs for good quality should never amount to as much as one per cent of the total production costs.

ADAPTING THE SEED PROCEDURES
FOR CERTIFYING FOODS

The U.S. seed certification services provide a model that mighty readily be adapted to assure the safety and quality of basic food products. What a boon it would have been, in the past three years, if a field service had assisted in production of honest organic foods, eliminating the fakes and the frauds. And what a blessing for progressive food retailers, to be able to offer certified fruits and vegetables to their quality-conscious customers!

These are the key relationships between seed and food product certification: Purity in seeds is similar to safety in foods, defined as relative freedom from DDT, PCB, arsenic, stilbestrol, antibiotics, mercury and other harmful elements; germination is similar to quality, as to mineral and vitamin contents, protein level, sugar-acid ratio and other nutritive and taste factors; varietal purity is similar to honesty in labelling as to whether the food products are true to their names, claims and labels.

There is the potential for a group of enlightened poultry growers or citrus or potato growers to support a nonprofit, private service to improve their products for acceptance by millions of quality-conscious food customers. They would form and run their food improvement associations with the assistance of capable food scientists, processors and food marketing people. This is a long overdue business development.

Such growers would register the product they wished to qualify for certification with their association. They would submit to field inspections of their production operations, and they would use only the production materials that would be acceptable for achieving a certification of the product. Samples would be taken in an orderly fashion and analyzed for safety and quality. Gas chromatography would be used to detect excessive amounts of chemical residues, such as DDT, arsenic and stilbestrol. Dry matter analyses would show the mineral composition of fruits and vegetables, and serve as the basic index to their quality. Blank spots would stand out like neon signs to expose growers who attempt to cheat in the production of their crops. The field inspections would show what crops are truly organic, and which are not.

The certification of a crop of Florida oranges might look like this:

Florida Food Crop Improvement Association

CERTIFICATE OF SAFETY & QUALITY

February 29, 1975

Product: Valencia Oranges
Grower: John Brown
       Route 3, Box 333
       Orlando, Florida

This certifies that Lot No. 1234 of Valencia oranges, produced by the above grower, has been inspected and tested by the Florida Food Crop Improvement Association, and that the following is a true report:

Sugar-acid ratio	12.6
Total solids as percent of total weight	15.2%
Vitamin C (ascorbic acid)	55 mg. per 100 g.
Pesticides:	less than .3 ppm

No chlorinated hydrocarbon materials were used in producing this crop. It was fertilized with the Full Nutrition Fertilizer Program No. 567, which is approved by this Association.

Signed:
       John Doe
       Director

Figure 1

The certification of a shipment of dressed poultry from Georgia might look like this:

Georgia Poultry Improvement Association

CERTIFICATION OF SAFETY & QUALITY

February 30, 1975

Product: Poultry Broilers
Grower: Poulpak, Inc.
Athens, Georgia

This certifies that Lot No. 5280 of poultry broilers produced by the above grower, has been inspected and tested by the Georgia Poultry Improvement Association, and that the following is a true report:

Chlorinated hydrocarbon substances
(DDT, PCB and other)   less than .3 ppm
Arsenic   none

These poultry were produced without the use of arsenical or other supplementary growth stimulants. The feed to weight gain ratio was approximately 3.1 to 1. The quality rating, in the Georgia Poultry Improvement Association scale of quality, is Excellent.

Signed:
John Doe
Director

Figure 2

These certificates would serve as passports of quality wherever these food products moved in U.S. commerce, just as Blue Tag Certified Kentucky Bluegrass seed moves in all U.S. markets as the premium grade. Few people ever question this quasi-private grading system. It is reliable, and very little cheating occurs. There is no reason why a similar system, used to assure safety and quality in foods, would not also work.

A cost differential surely will exist between supplies of guaranteed good quality foods and supplies of debased products. The certified merchandise may cost 10% more. Most of this cost difference will relate to the intrinsic value of the food itself, however, rather than representing the cost of the certifying service. Even at the retail level, this should never exceed one percent.

The costs of honesty in our society, when well organized and rewarded, are usually quite low.

GOVERNMENT RESPONSIBILITIES

The public food agencies, first of all, have their own pollution problem. They have a big job ahead of them cleaning out their own stables, and sweeping out the food drug and chemical company lobbyists who have been living in their corridors and anterooms. Their employees, particularly in the higher positions, need to re-learn who they work for, and who provides the paychecks. They can be half forgiven for past sins because we consumers have acted like quiet mice. We were seldom heard from. And in our government, those who do not get heard from do not get served.

The role of government, once the matter of loyalty is clear, is to redirect its policies and work so it assists in restoring the quality and safety of the national food supplies, and gives tangible help and leadership in getting millions of tons of organic wastes, and not just token amounts, back into agriculture. Such redirected activities begin through new interpretations of existing laws, through authorizations and public funds. We must use specific allotments of Economic Development Administration grants, loans and services to assist food producers who will make good food supply contracts, and who will undertake to install waste processing units. We must use Environmental Protection Agency resources to conduct essential research in organic waste processing that is specifically relevant to the wastes from the food industry; for example, in treating poultry and beef feedlot wastes with ureaform to make valuable organic based fertilizers or in the use of the resources of this Agency in establishing pilot and demonstration enterprises in these fields. We must use preferential Farmers Home Administration loan funds to assist growers who enter into good food production contracts. We must insist on a priority allocation of USDA and FDA research and technical resources to serve the development of a food quality and safety program of the kind we are discussing. We must set aside a specific portion of USDA's Agricultural Stabilization and Conservation funds ($3.6 billion in 1971) for payments to farmers who execute and fulfill good food production contracts and waste disposal covenants. This allocation should be on an ascending scale, until about 15% ($500 million) is set aside for these purposes.

Even such substantial allocations of public resources, and a redirection in governmental services, will still be insufficient, however, and at least one new public law will be needed.

A piece of basic legislation is needed that will offer federal support for state legislation and programs in food and organic waste disposal fields. This essential legislation can be based on the concepts of the Federal Agricultural Marketing Agreement Act of 1937 (Public Law 137), as amended. This law provides that when a majority of growers or producers in a trade area approve of a set of price and/or quality provisions, to prevail in their enterprise, a federal marketing order will be issued. They, in effect, make an internal agreement within their sector of the farm industry that becomes binding upon all of the producers, and that has public assistance in its operations and enforcement.

It is only a short step to adapting this Act to support an improvement in food safety and quality, and to obtain a mandatory processing and recycling of organic wastes back into agriculture.

Here are two hypothetical examples:

Waste Cycling

The poultry industry of Arkansas, let us say, has 600 major producers. They recognize that the wastes of their industry must be processed and adequately disposed of. No individual can afford to make the investment and pay the costs, however, because it would be business suicide. Even a majority of the group could be undercut by the minority, if the minority did not go along with the program and had lower production costs. A solution is still possible: (1) A competent study would be made to determine the quantities of wastes, their location, the proposed technology to use in processing them, the potential markets for the fully processed wastes, the best business arrangements for the new enterprise, the sources and costs of financing, the investment requirements, the annual net costs, and the costs per pound of poultry production, to finance the waste disposal operations. (2) The 600 members of the industry would consider the report and a plan of action and resolve their views about it. (3) They would inform the government that they wished to vote on the proposed program, under federal or state supervision, and see whether a majority of the members of the industry wished to make a Waste Disposal Agreement. (4) The plebiscite would then be held. If a stated percentage or majority of the producers, such as 60%, approved of the Agreement, the federal or state agency would issue an order, and the conditions of the new program would become binding on all members.

The Agreement might provide, for example, that ½¢ per pound of broilers and other poultry meats will be paid by the producers into a waste disposal fund, to establish and develop an effective waste processing operation. Arkansas markets about 1.7 billion pounds of birds annually. An anti-pollution business development fund of over $8 million per year would be established. Such a sum could well launch a successful program, since it should have diminishing net costs as the entire public begins to support its essential environmental programs. USDA, for example, will eventually find out who it works for, and begin to use its educational and technical supports for an increasing use of organic fertilizers in major crop production.

Food Improvement

The poultry industry of Georgia, let us say, has 800 producers. They recognize that an elimination of certain additives and other safety improvements, including mandatory quality control, are essential for the welfare of their industry.

They proceed in a manner similar to the one described above for Arkansas. They settle on the components and costs of their program, and the proposed levies within the industry to put it into effect. They vote. If a majority approves, the federal order is issued. The whole Georgia industry then must comply with the new Food Safety & Quality Agreement.

"Well," you may say, "how about these Georgia and Arkansas producers if the others in North Carolina, Mississippi, Alabama, Texas, and other places do not go along?

They are not yet bound by any agreements and orders."

That situation is a part of democracy, and there are ways to handle it, if democracy is working well. The enabling act can provide that, after the program is established, the federal purchases of poultry, including for the armed forces, must be made preferentially from the states that support the program and put it into effect. It can even provide for a premium in prices. There is a reason. The products of this program are safer and more suitable for the armed forces and for public agency use. Consumers may support the program by buying, in increasing amounts, the production of producers in the agreement areas.

These are tools of democracy if we only use them.

Making
Earth Foods

MANY THOUGHTFUL people are frightened today because food scientists seem to have learned too much about our basic foods, and how they are made. The food chemists have learned how to take apart corn, meats, milk, soy beans, peas or potatoes, for example, and then put the pieces back together again in new combinations, just like we used to do with Tinker Toys.

Then, presto, we have a new kind of food.

They are able to do such things because the staple foods are made, by plants and animals, out of our same old friends carbon, hydrogen and oxygen from the air, and the nitrogen and minerals from the soil. The plants put these elements together into about 23 basic building blocks, called amino acids. Then they construct proteins from these basic units. There is, however, a division of labor between plants and animals in making the various kinds of proteins. The plants construct the original building blocks, the amino acids and then their genes (heredity carriers) arrange them in proper order for making the vegetable proteins. The animals, including man, break the vegetable proteins back into simpler units, and then rearrange these to form the more complete animal proteins. The higher forms of animals, however, obtain some of their essential proteins in ready-made forms, from eating other creatures, such as fish, insects, birds and other animals.

This division of processes in protein synthesis, between plants and animals, forms the basis for the conventional food and dietary guides that have prevailed in the United States for many years. These guides were based on the fact that animals were more versatile than plants in making these essential foods units, and in general the animal proteins were superior for human use.

Conventional nutritionists and home economists have therefore advocated that human diets should always include animal proteins derived from meats, milk, eggs, fish, cheese and other such products. The modern food scientists have entered the scene, however, and removed the boundaries between animal and vegetable classes of foods. They have been able, for example, to break down beans, oats, wheat and corn into their basic components, and recombine these into new and superior protein clusters, that may be equal to high quality meat, and surely are superior to many of the mediocre meat products that are offered in today's markets; they can make good foods out of various combinations of vegetable and animal protein materials, thereby reducing the inherent costs of good protein foods; they may add amino acids, such as lysine and tryptophane, to cereals, thereby improving their values as human foods. They may add lysine to wheat flour, for instance, and double the protein value of the bread for only a few cents a loaf; they are able to grow bacteria on petroleum materials, since the fossil oils contain nitrogen, and then process the bacteria crop into animal foods; perhaps even into human foods.

At a different time in the American scene, such scientific developments might be reported in technical journals, but have a delayed influence in the food and restaurant trades.

Our situation, however, favors a quick movement of information on food innovations into the consumer food stream. Powerful forces are working. The costs of meat, milk, eggs, fish, poultry and related products are steadily rising. The quality of the traditional foods is declining, and consumers are interested in convenience foods which require a minimum of cooking and housework in their use.

These forces are shifting customers into acceptance of new kinds of ready-made foods, pizzas, instant breakfasts, TV dinners, canteen lunches, etc., and such foods can be fabricated from standardized components. They open the way for additional items that will appear in increasing volume in food stores and restaurants, such as:

Soyaburgers, made from combinations of meat and vegetable ingredients, that are superior to conventional hamburgers in flavor, aroma, cooking performance, and actual food value. The cost reduction may be about 25%.

Textured vegetable protein foods, made from soy and other vegetable materials, that act like natural meats and animal and poultry products, but are really from the lower cost sources.

High nutrition breads, cookies and pastries, made with additions of vegetable, milk, and fish protein materials, and with vitamin and mineral supplements.

Conventional breads and cereals, fortified with lysine and other amino acids to raise the nutritional levels.

Fortified beverages, as alternatives to the belly wash sodas that are overconsumed by all classes of Americans, especially children.

High nutrition snack bar, carry-out and convenience

foods, made with vegetable, milk, fish and other food components.

Food candies and confections, that taste good, are good for young people and children, and break the high sugar syndrome.

These examples illustrate significant trends in the American food scene, that may reduce the costs of good foods, but there are also awful possibilities.

There is an integrity in the natural forms of foods that comes through to the consumer, if food scientists and processors will just leave the natural forms alone. A carrot *is* a carrot, in this sense, no matter how poorly it is grown. The same holds for apples, cereal grains, milk, oranges, meats, and other basic food crops. Their genetic laws say that they have certain nutritional values and flavors. The organic and other good food rebels want to retain these values in the mainline food supplies of the country, and they do not trust the food industry, the Food and Drug Administration, or the U.S. Department of Agriculture with an opportunity to tamper with those values.

These people have a strong position, based on what has happened in recent years. They say, "Look what they did to bread, removing the good nutrients until it was a carbohydrate shell, then claiming to enrich it by putting back a few synthetic vitamins and minerals. Look what they did to chickens, adding arsenic, growth harmones and medications for quick profits, all with the sanction of FDA and USDA. Look what they did to red meats, with stilbestrol, sodium nitrate, and god knows what other chemicals that are being added in production and processing. Look what they did to hamburgers and hot dogs, raising the fat to over 50% and knocking down the protein to 8%. Look what they did to breakfast cereals, coating them with sugar like Christmas candy, and then raising the price to 75¢ a pound."

"How can you trust such people?" they say, "with an opportunity to take our basic foods apart and put them back together again, just like Tinker Toys? Consider the new dog and cat foods. No real meat and fish, anymore. Just 20 kinds of goop, all mixed up, squeezed out in funny shape, glued together, dyed, stabilized, preserved and scented so cats and dogs can't help but eat it."

These people have a real point, and their rising influence in food matters should not be underrated. U.S. food supplies have been debased, as we have seen, by poor fertilization of the crops, malnutrition of livestock and poultry, and the heedless adding of drugs and industrial chemicals into foods. A further debasing, by flooding the markets with high profit fabricated foods can only be counted as an awful possibility.

This could reduce America into being one of the worst fed nations of the world, rather than just a medium-poor one as we are now.

THE GOOD POTENTIALS IN MANUFACTURED FOODS

The food leaders of the organic and natural food persuasions have a tendency to see the situation through the eyes of fairly affluent white Americans, who can afford to be anxious about a flea in the flour or a speck in the stew. Millions of other Americans are not privileged to support such worries. They are lucky to get *any* hamburger, fat or lean. These more tolerant food shoppers, of the black, poor white, Mexican American, Puerto Rican, Indian and Eskimo communities, have a rising interest in good foods at low prices. You will not find them shopping for 60¢ a pound sesame seeds or simon pure health food bread, made from Deaf Smith Texas certified organic wheat. You will find them in the ghetto stores making food stamps stretch over beans, oatmeal, fat pork and mustard greens.

These diligent shoppers are joined in the search for good foods at low prices by thousands of young people who don't believe in modern advertising anymore. They are interested in quantity purchases of brown skinned rice and in the practical arts of making stew. Their potential influence upon the food industry is akin to their potential influence in U.S. politics: they are smart and realistic, and they will not follow traditional guides.

These ethnic, poor white and counter-culture groups make up about 44 million, about 21%, of the total U.S. population. They are concentrated in the inner cities, the core areas where they have moved from rural America since 1940. Twenty-three U.S. cities now have over 30% black populations. These are joined by Puerto Rican, Mexican American and Indian constituencies, most of which are also confined to the inner city areas.

These people have become a market force. They have different tastes, food preferences, income statuses and shopping incentives from the peer group that tends to concentrate in the suburbs. It is in this large and expanding group that we foresee an early acceptance of new full nutrition low cost foods. Let us examine several illustrations.

CORN SOY MILK (CSM) AND
WHEAT SOY BLEND (WSB)

Several leaders in U.S. overseas food programs decided, between 1965 and 1966, to develop low-cost full nutrition foods for foreign people that were being assisted by our

115

government in the Food For Peace programs. They placed a small advertisement in the journals of commerce inviting food companies to submit their proposals of the specifications and prices for such foods.

There was a common thought that appeared in many of the food company proposals that were received; namely, that these low cost foods should be combinations of: a cereal base, such as corn or wheat, concentrated protein materials, such as soy bean meal and dry milk solids, and essential vitamins and minerals. Many formulas were considered and tested. Two were developed into significant new food products. These were: corn-soy-milk (CSM), based on pre-cooked corn meal, soy meal, and non-fat dried milk, supplemented with vitamins and minerals. It is suitable to be cooked as a porridge, or mixed with milk or water and used as a nutritious beverage. Wheat-soy-blend (WSB) is based on wheat instead of corn, and has similar composition and nutritional values.

These foods have an inherent wholesale cost of about 10¢ a pound, packed in moisture-proof 50 pound bags. A great deal of experience in other countries has been acquired in using them to help both adults and children overcome malnutrition. They are, generally speaking, effective and acceptable as main components of a family's diet. About 1½ billion pounds of these low cost foods have been manufactured and supplied since 1966, to countries in our Food For Peace programs. Most of this was CSM, which was developed first. The wheat-soy-blend (WSB) is also gaining acceptance.

The success of these foods abroad raises the question: Why not adapt them for our domestic needs and markets, and use them here?

The Krause Milling Company of Milwaukee, one of the leading manufacturers of CSM for the foreign food programs, donated 80,000 pounds of this food to the USDA in 1970, for a test of its acceptance among public food program families in four southern counties located in Alabama, Florida and North Carolina. The product was packed in attractive 2 pound packages, along with directions for its use, and distributed to about 20,000 people, a majority of whom were black. A survey was then taken to get their reactions about the acceptability of the product. They were asked, "Would you like to continue getting the CSM for use by your family?"

About 83% answered, "Yes."

This acceptance rate was higher than for many of the old standby foods on the commodity distribution lists. It indicated that many of these low income homemakers are truly interested in better nutrition for their families. A special effort was made in three of the trial counties to tell the people about CSM's special nutritional values, and how to use it in a variety of ways. Where this was done, 9 out of 10 said they wanted more of this food material.

The interviewers in the survey were impressed by the interest of the families in improving their daily diets. Mother after mother commented that CSM seemed to make the children look and feel healthier.

"Yes, the children like it," one young mother said, "It helps their skin to look good and their teeth to say white." Another observed, "It is good for their eyes and health. It's helping the children to feel better."

These people tried CSM. They learned to like it when they were told of its nutritional values. The public food agencies are now pondering the results of this trial, wondering whether to depart from conventional foods and offer such new items as CSM in our own domestic food programs.

The much larger vista which should be seen is the

adaptation of these versatile products for Americans who are getting priced out of the good food markets, the poor whites, blacks, yellows, browns, young and old, those who seem to be becoming the majority as food prices steadily rise.

As the wheels turn this large group of Americans will look at the glamorous TV food ads with dimmer eyes. They will learn more about foods and nutrition, and have a rising interest in such good low cost products as CSM and WSB.

THE BLACKWELL FOOD PROJECT

Mr. Randolph Blackwell, a most versatile, durable and practical black business development leader of the rural south, refuses to be defeated or to share defeat with his people. He is the Director of Southern Rural Action, Inc., of Atlanta, Georgia.

Between 1968 and 1969, Mr. Blackwell led the nation's most significant rural food project, in upgrading the nutrition of a whole county full of people, affluent and poor, but mostly poor, since Taliaferro County, Georgia is one of the poorest counties in the nation: 60% black, 75% unemployed, smashed by the mechanization of the cotton industry.

The whole county was provided with assured access to adequate good foods and pharmaceuticals, even vitamins and baby formulas for six months, and were given intensive food education and transportation necessary to get the foods and the education. Medical examinations were then made, before and after, by a team of 40 doctors and paramedical personnel. The resulting report, which offered guides for improving our country's public and private food programs, was of interest to Dr. Jean Mayer, head of the

White House Food and Nutrition Conference of 1969, who bought 400 copies for its use.

Randolph Blackwell has been working without resources, to carry the Taliaferro County guides into practical large scale food projects. He purchased a bakery, hired a young GI baker, and sent his baker to the Meals for Millions cooking school at Santa Monica, California. The objective was to launch a successful production of fortified cookies, breads, soups and other foods to meet the demands for better foods at reasonable prices.

"My people need such foods and wish to buy them," says Blackwell. "We need the market volume, however, of the school lunch programs, institutions, and other state and federal purchases to get this timely business enterprise off the ground. I want to see fortified cookies and bread in every public school lunch, and in the lunch buckets where there are no school lunch programs. We can then say, 'Eat all the cookies you like,' to the children, 'they are good for you.'"

FOOD ADAPTATION FOR INNER-CITY PEOPLE—NIGERIAN STYLE

The tragic Nigerian civil war decimated the Ibo people and left a terrible toll in starvation and malnutrition of the people of both sides, particularly children. When it ended, an international effort was made to assist the people in overcoming this malnutrition. Our government contributed several thousand tons of CSM and WSB for use in the damaged areas. But there was a problem. The Nigerian people had never heard of these foods, and they did not have the foggiest idea how to use them. They might be disinclined to accept them.

Arrangements were therefore made by the U.S. manufacturers of the WSB and CSM to conduct food adaptation work, assisted by competent Nigerian students and professionals from Washington, D.C. These people, carefully selected, were fully acquainted with the food customs, recipes and attitudes of the needy people of their homeland. The authors were employed to design and handle the food adaptation project. Interestingly enough, the operations attracted the attention and participation of several capable leaders in Washington's inner city urban renewal programs, including Dr. Stephen Dippe, Medical Director of the Redevelopment Land Agency.

We studied, with the help of the Nigerian food advisers, the main meal diets and customs of the people of the war torn communities. These studies disclosed that a dish called foo foo was a main meal food, known to and eaten by all inhabitants of the areas. It is usually made from cassava, which is nearly 100% carbohydrate, with little or no protein, vitamins and minerals for repairing malnourished bodies.

Cassava was mixed on a 50-50 basis with wheat-soy-blend and cooked in the traditional way for eating with the traditional soups and sauces of the Nigerians. It became a fully acceptable 10% protein dish that was preferable, even in blindfold tests, to the straight cassava. Good guide recipes were then made, exploring various opportunities to use both WSB and CSM in dishes that are commonly eaten by Nigerian people. An upgrading of nutrition was assured in every case.

We held a foo foo feast in Washington, D.C. at the close of this work. It was attended by our Nigerian advisers and friends, and by our inner city urban renewal program leaders. Dr. Stephen Dippe of the Redevelopment Land Agency made a statement:

Allow me to say, that attempts to change the intake and culinary habits of inner city people are more than likely going to meet with very poor success unless strong and forceful efforts are made to improve food production and distribution. It is my belief that the only way to strengthen and improve the dietary intake of this population is to improve and enrich the already accepted foods and if possible remove the non-fortified foods which may not only be useless but dangerous to one's health. I would like to emphasize that I am very enthusiastic about the food adaptation project for the inner city, since I think we have a community here that is willing, ambitious, desirous, wanting, and more important asking to improve their own nutrition and as a result our society.[9]

MAKING EARTH FOODS—A PRACTICAL VIEW

In foods, as in atomic energy, sex and fertilizers, some things are here to stay. The use of science and inventions will not be denied. The formulated, taken-apart, put-together-again foods are here to stay.

The questions are: Who will reap the benefits? Who may get hurt? How can we distribute the values of low cost foods among dollar-short customers, rather than have these products exploited, adulterated, lied about, mislabelled and over-priced?

The answers will be formulated by active consumers and the food industry, with FDA and Agriculture trailing along as usual, seeing where the power is before they act.

The problem is to get the good low cost products into the main food stream for millions of ordinary eaters, to get soyaburger, for example, into the supermarkets and hamburger palaces, and to get the reduced costs actually passed

[9] Dr. Stephen Dippe, Medical Director, Redevelopment Land Agency. (Letter to Lee Fryer, March 12, 1970).

on to the customers in the form of reduced prices. This miracle of reducing food prices during inflation can happen if organized customers help future-minded food company leaders to make it that way. What it takes is business imagination and realism, since this is the biggest field for sound food market expansion: offering good, full nutrition foods to medium and low income customers at low prices. That is where the action is.

We foresee within 10 years whole new lines of manufactured food products catering to this expanding dollar-conscious market, such as:

Formulated milk, that is clean, free of added chemicals, fully nutritious as a milk, for a retail price of 25¢ a quart. The U.S. dairy cow is, figuratively speaking, headed for the Smithsonian Institution and various zoos. The labor and capital costs are too high for use in producing this hallowed fluid as a staple food item. Also, the cows are too short-lived and unhealthy in the artificial milk factory environments. Milk, like hamburger, chickens and many other natural foods, is so debased that it isn't worth defending on a purist basis. We need a new milk-like product for the main U.S. market demand. Pure milk will be an ingredient.

A 50–50 soyaburger food, half good hamburger meat and half vegetable materials. It'll be juicy, won't shrink, a superior product. Price: 75¢ a pound in supermarkets, and at 10¢ less for medium sized hamburgers at hamburger places.

A crunchy granola breakfast food, blended from unmilled seeds, rolled oats, nuts, raisins, oil and honey, made popular among children by full spectrum advertising and food education.

U.S. adapted wheat-soy-blend and corn-soy-milk as

staple low cost foods. Price: about 25¢ a pound retail in 5 pound packages.

Spectrum soups, freeze dried, containing all of the original food factors in vegetables and meats, saving the high value soup stock. To be promoted for good low cost whole meals.

The packaging and labelling of these good low cost foods will be vital, and sound guides will be needed. It is ridiculous to offer a 25¢ per pound product in a package that costs 20¢, particularly when it has a deceptive label. Consumer union guides exist and can be fully developed to assist the food industry in coping with their packaging and labelling problems, which have gotten out of hand. Competitive pressures in the absence of consumer support of sound packaging and labelling practices have created chaos.

Are we shooting too high with these objectives for 1980 or not high enough?

Any society that was able, without fuss or fanfare, to put the peace sign on children's clothing, flags, toys and bicycles is able to put tomatoes and dry milk in soda if they wish to put it there.

We are a strange people. We finally have it so that good water costs more per gallon than gasoline. What next?

CHAPTER EIGHT

Earth Kitchens

EARTH KITCHENS are places where you cook good foods, using the arts and recipes that have come down through the ages or just a Betty Crocker cookbook.

There are generally two kinds of cooks, as far as the use of recipes is concerned—those who follow the book, word for word, and the happy types who just sing away, throw in two more eggs, some more flour when it's too soupy, some more milk when it's took thick, a dash of oregano, some parsley flakes to make it pretty, and a couple of glups of molasses.

Once we asked a lady how she made such good gingerbread. "Oh, I put in this and that and then about 10 glups of molasses."

"What is a glup of molasses?" we asked.

"Oh," she said, "it's when you tip up the bottle like this and the molasses comes out, glup, glup, glup."

There is little doubt that these informal, experimental cooks have left big footprints in the corridors of history. An ancient Egyptian invented yeast and the processes of fermentation over 5,000 years ago, probably because it rained in his grain pot while he dallied too long with the neighbor's daughter. So Egypt had leavened bread and beer for all those years while the poor Romans had to eat mush.

Which brings us to the interesting subject of who invented johnnycakes in the U.S.

We believe johnnycakes were invented by a Tennessee mountaineer named Johnny, who broke his oven in about 1830 and couldn't bake bread. He mixed flour, water, salt, sugar and baking powder together and cooked it in his frying pan on top of the stove, golden brown on one side and black brown on the other. He ate it morning and night, and took the habit with him to Oregon, where he settled on the grassy banks of the Yamhill River. The johnnycakes spread north from there to the Klondike and south to tortilla country, over the cattle trails and into the mining camps, and then to the farms and ranches.

Everyone knew about johnnycakes. You could mix them thick or you could mix them thin, but they were always about the same because they were so fundamental, just an earth bread fried on a campfire or on top of the stove.

The years came and went. The western housewives baked biscuits and light bread, and johnnycakes became a man's food for him to cook and eat when he was camping, hunting, fishing or travelling with livestock. He would make one at evening time from the flour, water, salt, sugar and baking powder, and have a fine meal. The hard crust connoisseurs ate the edges and the soft bread men ate the middles with butter or bacon gravy.

Johnnycakes were the earth food that never quite came into the house.

Johnnycakes lurked in the edges of the western settlements like measles breaking out here and there on camping expeditions, until the mixed up 1920's, when thousands of working men became railroad bums. They were bindle stiffs, loggers, floaters, hard rock miners, IWW's, bonus marchers, harvest workers and city kids out to see the country. No women. These men rode around free, as un-invited guests of the railroads, in empty boxcars, in the blinds between the coaches, on the engine tenders, on top, and even on the brace rods underneath the cars, except for the stumble bums. They preferred to walk on the railroad tracks. "We're not going anyplace anyway," they said, "and we've got lots of time."

The jungles were the camping places for the railroad bums. They were organic. They just grew at logical places, such as under tressles, on river banks, in the woods by the creek, or near a water tower. By the 1930's, in the Great Depression, these places became vital to the operation of the country, when a million men were traveling around looking for work. They were the outdoor earth kitchens of the railroad-riding depression bums, and they were johnnycake country.

Two foods prevailed in the jungles, johnnycakes and stew. The better jungles had resident managers, self-appointed and self-accepted. They lived there by common consent, and ran the places. On a typical day, the popula-tion dwindled quickly after breakfast. The men scattered and hopped on the trains like fleas to a new dog, except for 15 or 20 who rested, repaired their clothes and gear, and helped to tidy up the place. Then at 4 or 5 o'clock in the afternoon, when the freight trains came through, the new bums came tumbling off. They were curtly greeted by the jungle boss, who said, "Gimme your grub." This meant you had to give him all the food you had, or go on your way. The men knew this, even while they had been gathering cabbages, meat, onions, rabbits, carrots, flour, salt, sugar, bacon, chickens, sweet rolls, turnips, firewood —all kinds of plunder.

They gave it to the jungle boss. He ran the kitchen with a volunteer crew. They used several open fires and improvised stoves made from sheet metal. The pots were 5 gallon cans. The entrée was mullagatawney stew. That means everything went in after being dressed, cleaned and prepared in a practical way.

The staple bread was johnnycake, cooked in big frying pans, or on sheet metal.

Crude courtesies and cleanliness prevailed, enforced by the old bums and the IWW's, who revered women, children, soap, water and a clean camp and hated bosses but respected each other. They taught the young and careless how to act when they transgressed, or kicked them out of the jungle. After eating, you rested, smoked, talked low and slept on the ground.

That was the U.S. jungle, very organic, so organic that settled folk a quarter of a mile away hardly knew it was there and didn't care.

A YOUNG PEOPLES' EARTH KITCHEN

Our hearts are troubled about the young folk of today, who sense that our outmoded cities will fail and who are trying to learn how to live in open country. Most of them have no skills or spleen for this kind of thing. Their fathers were never railroad bums. It takes, as all good bums gradually learn, a hard and tender philosophy of life and a deep respect for a cake of soap. A *crummy* bum is the world's most wretched creature. (You are crummy when your body dirt gets thick enough so it rolls up into little crumbs. You are then both organic and dirty.)

For whatever value it may be to these young pilgrims, we will set up an outdoor earth kitchen and cook a great meal.

Here are the tools and the ingredients:

2 pails or cut-down 5-gallon cans, or other big cans.
2 grates, or wire racks, like you get out of ovens.
1 frying pan, big and heavy unless you are back-packing.
Nails and a hammer, to pound into trees and other places, to hang things on.
A big roll of paper towels or clean cloths.
Knives, forks and spoons, and big spoons or stirring sticks. Also, plates, cups and things to eat on.
A shovel.
8 or 10 stones, bricks or hunks of metal, to make supports for your grates.
Matches and firewood.
Soap.
Some meat (unless you are a vegetarian): beef, pork, sheep, rabbit, chicken, wild game, birds.
Some vegetables: potatoes, onions, carrots, turnips, yams, celery, green peppers.
Salt and pepper.
Water, of course.

You build two fires. It is easiest if you build the big fire first. Then you lay up the rocks or bricks to hold up the grate for your smaller fire, about 10 or 15 feet away. Let the big fire burn awhile, as you sing, make camp, fiddle around, look at the sky, rub smoke out of your eyes, wash your hands, whatever. Then shovel live coals from the bottom of the big fire over to your other fireplace, and get it going without much wood. Keep it small, mostly coals. Install the grate on top of the rocks or bricks, and then put on one pail or can half full of water.

Cut up the meat and throw it in the water. Boil it for an hour or so, and then throw in the vegetables, which you have peeled, cleaned and fixed to suit yourself. Hold such things as the cabbage until the stew is nearly done, because cabbage takes only 15 or 20 minutes to cook. Salt and pepper it to suit yourself.

While all of this is going on, let your big fire burn down enough so you can stick 3 or 4 bricks or rocks in one side to hold up the other pail or 5 gallon can. Then, set the can or pail, three-fourths full of water, on these. Fire up again, to suit yourself. This is your kitchen hot water supply, don't wash your dirty hands and face in it.

Make coffee or tea, if you want, as you go along.

Eat your dinner. Love it. Pick out different kinds of pieces that you like together such as carrots, turnips and meat and use some broth and butter on your potatoes with plenty of pepper. Great!

The human creature, frail though he may be, lives because of other human beings. We are a species that thrives only if we assist one another. We are destined, in this sense, always to be a community, if we survive.

An earth kitchen may replenish these values for you, because you seldom make and use it alone. It is for use with others, your wife, companion, children or a group, but it is best small. Otherwise, you may find yourself working too hard and losing the sense of nearness of nature.

THE INDOOR-OUTDOOR KITCHEN

This is the one we have been working up to for 400 or 500 years in America. It is located in a house where the boundary between indoors and outdoors cannot be found. Each blends into the other. The kitchen, of course, is the interface and the way to make sure is to put one fire and quite a lot of living outside.

Weather is not a problem. It is a condition. Omelets and

johnnycakes are not so good when they are rained on, so you cook them inside on rainy days. Rain, cold, heat and wind are good to feel and see so you can deepen your feelings and live better. One of the homiest of all feelings is sitting under a tight roof eating your dinner and watching it rain. This fattens the soul.

It is only the young and the inexperienced who wish for cooking and living to be difficult, without electricity, refrigeration, good stoves, pots, dishes, cabinet space, running water and trash disposal. The architects of our time should work on the problem of the indoor-outdoor house with all these conveniences but with the shared outdoor space reducing the cost of the indoor part.

As to the foods for indoor-outdoor living, for earth cooks to use in the spacious kitchens, that run two miles over the hill, it is impossible to see them as other than safe and good. Good housing and good foods, at low cost, can come only back-to-back. The same minds and spirits that produce one will produce the other.

CHAPTER NINE 🎜

Earth Food Cooking

EARTH FOOD cooking has a central idea that we will illustrate in this chapter. It is the idea of one-ness and whole things: whole foods, whole people, full nutrition, great combinations, full flavor, a whole earth.

For too long the forces of our mechanized society have had the opposite impact, to shatter, separate, fabricate, remove, pasteurize, sanitize, destroy. Hence our longing to be put together again as a people.

Foods and cooking are among our deepest symbols. It is no accident that in the Christian faiths, for example, there was a Last Supper and a Sacrament, an eating and drinking to the deepest wish in a person's life.

We have come to a desperate place in America when we have to put the fruits and vegetables back together again, take vitamins, eat supplements, reconstitute the milk, analyze the chickens, and put the germs back into the wheat and corn seeds. That is where we are, however, and it will be a long time until another day.

Earth food cooking is an experience in making things whole again. Relax and enjoy it. Worry only about the soul, in foods and in us. If it flutters, we will overcome.

☙ THE STOCK POT

The stock pot is sort of a cook's compost pile in a well-run earth food kitchen. It is a device for recycling the minerals, vitamins and proteins of a kitchen to the people of the house. The size of the pot will vary with the family. A two-gallon size is good for a household of 4 or 5 people.

Cooking stocks, historically, have been the foundation for many dishes for hearty people. They helped in making the soups, stews, gravy, and starch-vegetable-meat combinations of various ethnic societies. Whether rich or poor, the people savored these soupy foods and enjoyed their low costs. Mid-century America went the other way, to the eating of unadorned muscle meats with a few accessories: steaks, hamburgers and french fries bought with credit cards.

We are moving into another era, however, when the price of good food is becoming a vital matter and a knowledge of nutrition is permeating the homes and organizations of all people. The intelligent housewife says, "I cannot afford the good meats and the expensive fruits and vegetables, anymore. Where will I get enough vitamins, minerals and proteins for my family?"

The young in the communes say, "We need a good rich liquor to use in cooking our rice and beans. Let's save the vegetable juices."

We are moving again in America toward the acceptance of boiled foods, and of dishes that utilize cooking liquors in their preparation.

Such cooking stocks, classically, come in four kinds, brown, white, pure vegetable, and fish. The old French rules defined these carefully, and were very fussy about such horrors, for instance, as mutton in the white stock, which we may deal with later.

Bones are the prime ingredient in earth food meat and vegetable stock. They have the marrow, calcium, gristle, sinews, soft discs, collagens and gelatine, that are rich and good for you. Table scrap bones will help, but you also will need good fresh ones. They are available, even in a supermarket, and if not there, at a kosher meat market. Ask for them. Tell the man you have a big dog named Rover, and go back again and again. Buy them, don't beg them, you are a proud dog.

The secret is that the mild acids of the vegetables will dissolve some of the proteins and the lime of the bones will buffer these mild acids. Your cooking stock will then have slight amounts of free amino acids subtly influencing the flavor and adding nourishment for all sizes and ages. You need:

A 2 gallon pot	Turnips
Bones	Summer squashes
Celery butts	1 teaspoon of salt
Onion tops	per quart of water
Cabbage leaves	1 tablespoon of peppercorns
Vegetable and fruit peelings	3 or 4 bay leaves
Snap bean ends	A pinch of rosemary
Pea pods	Other spices to
Okra and pepper stems	suit your fancy
Tomato skins and cores	Lemon and grapefruit rinds
Rutabagas	

To perform this miracle, pack the big kettle half full of bones and meat trimmings. Then top these with any assortment of vegetable items you can lay your hands on, such as celery butts, celery and onion tops, cabbage leaves, vegetable and fruit peelings, snap bean ends, pea pods, okra and pepper stems, tomato skins and cores, and stray rutabagas, turnips and summer squashes. Such items can be accumulated for a week in the refrigerator.

Add enough water to cover nearly everything, and put in about 1 teaspoon of salt per quart. Then add the peppercorns, bay leaves, rosemary leaves, and any other condiments and spices you like.

It is time now to get a new meaning for the old word: simmer. Simmering is not boiling. It occurs at 180 degrees Farenheit, at sea-level. The water at this temperature vaporizes at the bottom of the kettle, close to the heat, and rises, carrying its heat up through the bones and into the vegetables, warming them until they are 180 degrees too. This temperature is sufficient to break the cell membranes in the meat and vegetables, so their nutritious contents go out to join the crowd.

The length of simmering is not too important, as long as there is lots of it. Eight hours is a good time for many kinds of heat, but avoid hard boiling, just use this gentle kind.

When you have simmered for 2 hours throw in some lemon and grapefruit rinds, 2, 3 or 4. Check the taste and adjust with your favorite seasonings. Then complete the simmering for its full course.

Take the pot off to cool at room temperature when this stage of cooking is finished. The cooling will set the fat. Skim it off, and save it for making soups if the idea appeals to you. Otherwise, throw the fat away and stay slim.

Reheat the stock and strain it through a collander. Put the solids on your compost pile or into the garbage. Save the strained stock.

An alternative is to strain the whole mass including the fat while it is still hot, and skim off the fat later when the liquid is cool. The delicious remainder, in either case, is your earth food cooking stock. Let it jell and use it in a dozen ways. It is good to eat straight and to use for cooking rice, stews, soups, dry peas, beans, potatoes, and many other things.

> Happy is the kitchen that has a stock pot.
> Its people get fat when the others do not.

❧ PAPAS—*Solanum Tuberosum*

People who have lived or travelled in Latin American countries know that potatoes are papas.

The waiter says, "Papas, senorita?"

You say, "Sí, señor, papas."

This name for potatoes probably came from the early Inca regions, pre-dating the Spanish conquest, since that is where potatoes were domesticated. When it crossed the Atlantic, however, *s. tuberosum* had its name changed. *Papa*, the Pope, was too sacred to share the name with an earthy vegetable.

So the Italians named it a sort of a truffle, since both truffles and potatoes grew under the ground. They called it "tortuffo" while the name for a truffle was "tortufi."

The French, as the potato moved North, changed the name to "cartouflo" and the Germans made it into "kartoffel." The Welch, having mastered the art of impossible town names, reversed their form and called the potato "cloron." This meant earth-root not a household bleach.

The colonists further clouded the scene by calling the sweet potato a "patata" or "batata." Poor old *s. tuberosum* got caught in that net, too. It became a "patata." Wherever it went, it got a new name.

The Irish, to whom potatoes were especially generous, launched the names Murphy's, O'Brien's and Gleeson's. These were the names of some successful Irish potato farmers. The Scots, who chose to call a spade a spud, named the potato from that tool.

In the southern United States, the more tropical sweet potato was better adapted than *s. tuberosum*, and better liked, so the people of Dixie, in a rather derogatory way, named the "patata" the Irish potato, pronounced with a wrinkled nose.

Such is the saga of *s. tuberosum*, our "papa," who is usually reduced to fat filled chips and the ubiquitous french fries. Let us see what we can do to rescue him.

Three great varieties of potatoes are available, in our present day and time, for the American cuisine. The Kennebec is the starchy fellow for french fries and potato chips. It is grown in Maine as well as in the western potato growing areas, and often is seen in food markets. The Burbank Russet, also called Netted Gem or Idaho Baker, is the superior baking and mashing kind. It too, is widely distributed. You can tell it by the mesh "net" of its skin, which is quite noticeable when the plant is well fertilized, but which almost disappears when the farmer uses too much nitrogen to boost the yield. The Pontiac, a roundish red variety, is fine for boiling. It has superb flavor and a waxy texture that potato buffs enjoy.

You will do well to teach your food market manager about these kinds of potatoes. Start by asking him, "Who gets all of the good potatoes, since we never get any good ones here?" Then pick up a bag of U.S. number 1's and say, "We used to use these for marbles where I came from." Then you can mention Kennebecs, Russets and Pontiacs. He will probably say, "Huh, I'll bet you never had any Katahdins from Maine." Then you have him hooked. He will have to get you some, and they are really fine potatoes.

◄§ PAPAS SALAD

Let us use, for our first potato recipe, 3 large Pontiacs. If you cannot get this variety, don't give up. Use any good potatoes. Peel them and put the peelings into the vegetable trimmings bag for making stock. Slice the peeled potatoes into strips 3 or 4 inches long. They will be 1 inch wide and 1 inch thick.

Plop these potato strips into a boiling cooking stock. Remember, you made it yesterday. Use salted water if no cooking stock is available. Then drop the heat, and poach the potatoes for 40 or 50 minutes at a simmering temperature. Drain off the stock and chill the potatoes. You'll note that cooked this way Pontiacs will never get soft and mushy, even on the surface.

Next, slice the potatoes cross-ways about as thin as poker chips, and marinate them overnight in water containing the juice of a lemon. Already, you will notice that they have a fine flavor.

Improve this by making a dressing of:

¼ cup of chopped chives	½ teaspoon of salt
1 tablespoon of lemon juice	1 teaspoon of dry mustard
1 raw egg, beaten with a fork	a few drops of tabasco sauce

Whiz this concoction around in a blender, and then add a tablespoon of your favorite cooking oil, olive, peanut, safflower or other. Then add another spoon of oil and whiz again in the blender until all of the ingredients form a runny sort of mayonnaise. This is your dressing. Pour it over the drained potato slices. Toss lightly and refrigerate for a few hours while the potatoes absorb the dressing. The taste is elegant.

❧ POTATO OMELET

This potato dish is substantial enough to act as a main meal item, and the cost is very low. It is so well established in some parts of Spain and other Latin countries that it will be served to you if you order a Spanish omelet. Here is the recipe:

Olive oil	1 clove of garlic
8 medium potatoes	4 eggs
3 onions	

Prepare a large, heavy frying pan or baking dish and add a scant cup of olive oil or other good cooking oil. Then peel 8 medium-sized potatoes. Wash in salt water and slice fairly thin and small. Cut up 3 medium-sized onions, also, into fairly small pieces. Add a chopped clove of garlic to taste. Mix the potatoes, onion and garlic together and salt moderately. Then put the mixture into the hot frying pan. Pat down evenly, and cover. Cook on a low flame until the potatoes can be pierced with a fork. Add oil if needed to keep them well lubricated.

Meantime, while the potatoes are cooking, beat 4 whole eggs in a large bowl. Then, turn the cooked potato-onion-garlic mixture into the eggs. Fold and mix together.

Oil the frying pan again, and put the whole mixture back into it. Then cook on a low flame until it is light golden brown on the bottom, still using the cover. Invert it, when done, onto a platter, so the golden side is up. Or if a baking dish is used and you wish to cook it that way, you may cook it in the oven during the last cooking, after the eggs have been added.

If desired, the omelet can be served with a sauce made by simmering onions, green peppers, mushrooms, tomato and green olives. Add salt and pepper to taste.

❧ CRUNCHY GRANOLA

Karl Marx discovered a hundred years ago that the ruling class plants the seeds for its own destruction. Vladimir Lenin harvested such a crop in Russia in 1917. The breakfast cereal barons of America planted their seeds of destruction between 1950 and 1970, in rows 3,000 miles long labelled Wheaties, Sugar Pops, Sugar Frosted Flakes, Kix, Alphabits, etc. The coup that ends their reign is *crunchy granola.*

This incendiary stuff, for the edification of people who never get across the railroad tracks, is what those hairy hippies are carrying around in their pouches and shoulder bags. It is food. Recently, caches of it have been found in drug and department stores across the country, and it is selling like mad. Also, thousands of otherwise normal women are sending crunchy granola recipes to one another like chain letters and giving the stuff to their husbands and children.

The theory of crunchy granola is that whole seeds, grains, nuts and raisins are good for you. It is an attractive mixture of such things, anointed with honey and oil, and baked so it is crunchy to eat. It contains quite a bit of oats, since as livestock men know, oats are a superior fitness food.

You can eat crunchy granola straight, chased with milk, water, beer, or other beverages, or you can eat it like any other cereal for breakfast. If it is around your house or office, you will find yourself nibbling on it all day, and the benefit on the bowels is very salubrious. Girls that take a quart of it to their offices become popular, since co-workers stop in for a handful, and the boss is usually among the freeloaders.

Here is a good crunchy granola recipe. Use organic or non-organic ingredients, as fits your faith and opportunities for buying such things.

7 cups of oatmeal, of the old-fashioned kind (not instant)	½ cup of sliced almonds
	1 cup of raw cashew nuts
	½ cup of honey
1 cup of coconut, shredded	¼ cup of a good cooking oil
¾ cup of raw shelled sunflower seeds	1 cup of wheat germ
½ cup of raw sesame seeds	1 cup of raisins

Mix the oatmeal, coconut, sunflower seeds, sesame seeds, almonds and cashews together. Pre-mix the honey and the cooking oil. Then mix these with the dry ingredients, above. Roast the raisins lightly, for 5 or 10 minutes in a 300 degree oven. Add them and the wheat germ, and mix the whole.

Spread about ¾ inch thick on cookie sheets and bake at 325 degrees for 10 or 15 minutes, or until the top is toasted a golden brown. Cool it, and tuck it away in cookie jars or where-ever you wish.

The cooking process is adequate to roast the raw seeds and cashew nuts.

❧ FISH

Most fish in our markets are superior foods, despite the mercury scares. The ocean-running kinds grow in a nutrient world, full of 60 minerals and the essentials for building good proteins. In this sense, fish are a near-perfect food, in sharp contrast to land-living creatures who are lucky to get half of a full diet, and to the food crops when they are so malnourished by farmers.

Any family that eats fish once a week is getting a boost

in its diet. The more of the whole fish that is eaten, the better. This accounts for the nutritional superiority of oysters, clams, shrimp and whole small fishes compared with fillets. Also, when a fish is poached or boiled, you get the extra juices and goodies that might be discarded from a fillet. A boiled fish's head, according to Jewish folklore, will nourish your brain and help you to overcome.

Bouillabaisse is the high point of boiled fish foods—diversified, tasty, rich and good. Its essence is in the blending of an assortment of both finned and shellfish. Saffron must be a principal condiment. Leeks, tomatoes and olive oil will be ingredients. Wine will be added. Several dreamy concoctions can be made on such a chassis. The clam and crab shells can be left in or out. Codfish can be featured. Halibut is better. Red snapper is good. Salmon is optional.

The kind we will make omits the shells. You'll be able to eat it with a spoon, but we will extract the flavors and humors from those shells in a preliminary cooking operation. Here is a good recipe:

Begin at the fish market. Buy a brace of halibut steaks. Also buy about 3 pounds of any combination of red snapper, pompano, sea bass or chum salmon or any other food fish that particularly strikes your fancy. Then buy or get:

>   2 pounds of medium large uncooked shrimp, deheaded
>   2 pounds of cooked crab in the shell
>   1 pound of clams: diced canned ones will do
>   1 pound of fresh shucked oysters
>   1 lobster, if easily available
>   2 squids, if easily available
>   ½ pound of mushrooms
>   1 package of frozen lima beans (or fresh ones)
>   1 bottle of chablis or grey riesling wine
>   1 large (or 2 medium) stalks of celery

    3 medium onions
    3 carrots
    4 tomatoes
    4 large leeks
    2 garlic cloves
    other condiments as mentioned below

You start building this bouillabaisse by making a court bouillon out of all the trimmings of the fish and vegetables. Into a big pot put the leaves and butt of the celery, the carrot skins and trimmings, the onion skins and butt slices, the leek roots and trimmings, all the fish trimming and the crab and shrimp shells. Add 2 quarts of water, juice of one lemon and a nickel-sized piece of lemon peel. Then, 1 tablespoon of salt, 13 peppercorns (for luck), a handful of parsley and a bay leaf.

Bring this stock to a boil, and then let it simmer for 1 hour. Strain it off into the main cooking pot in which you will make the bouillabaisse, a big one of about 8 quart size, if you can manage it. Then discard the debris, into your compost or garbage.

From now on, you construct the bouillabaisse with a timed addition of the various ingredients, so when the count-down is completed each item is perfectly cooked and blended into the whole.

Begin by adding the clam juice, a small matter, but the fairy goddess of cooking would be able to tell the difference. Then mash the garlic cloves and add them so they can do their mischief. Cut the celery into half inch pieces and add it. Bring the pot to a simmering boil. Ten minutes later, add the onions, coarsely chopped, and the sliced carrots. Let these mellow in the broth for 15 minutes more, and then add the 4 peeled and quartered tomatoes.

Prepare the halibut by cutting it into 2 by 2-inch slices.

Add the lima beans and the sliced leeks. Then, add the snapper and the other finny fish, first cutting into serving pieces.

Let it all poach for another 15 minutes. Add the oysters. Cut them in two if they are extra large. Add 1½ cups of the white wine. Save two tablespoons of it, however for rubbing into the saffron. Do this by mashing two big pinches of the saffron in the bottom of a cup with the wine. Then throw this into the pot.

Now, the crab and the shrimp. Put them in and stir until the shrimp are red. Then draw off a sample and taste it for seasoning. Correct the salt, and add one-fourth of a teaspoon of tabasco sauce. Stir again, and the bouillabaisse is ready to serve.

Big soup bowls are appropriate. Each person can select what looks good and then fill his bowl with the juice. A garnish of chopped celery hearts and parsley can act as a topping if one is desired.

The big pot will serve 8 hungry people, or a dozen city-weakened ones. It will still taste good warmed over.

❧ FISH SAUSAGES

We include this piece since times are changing, and quite a few pilgrims are developing low cash living systems in which they need to harvest things and then tide them over until next season.

The basic technology for making fish sausages is very similar to that which was used for centuries in Scandinavia, Holland and elsewhere. It involves a beneficent fermentation, and the use of drying, smoking and spicing. Dutch salted herring, still excellent, illustrates the process. In salads, with apples and potatoes, or as main dishes, their

Earth Foods

salty-fermented goodness is akin to that in fine finnan-
haddie, or well made lox of salmon. The briny fermentation, to those who like this kind of thing, improves the
flavor and texture of the fish.

When making fish sausages, particularly in a warm
season that could hasten spoilage, it is best to accelerate
the processes of fermentation, so the desired acidity level
can be quickly reached. This involves a conversion of the
sugars into lactic acid, a complex little task done by a
friendly kind of bacteria, best purchased from Merck &
Company, 9199 Red Branch Road, Columbia, Maryland
21043.

The following recipe is a good one:

Prepare 100 pounds of boneless fish fillets, and grind to
¼ inch size (¼ inch plate on the grinder). Then add:

> 2 pounds of high quality salt. (Do not use local solar salt)
> 1 pound and 2 ounces of sugar. (Raw sugar may be used)
> 1 tin of bacterial innoculant (check with Merck's)
> 2 ounces of ground pepper
> 1 ounce of ground allspice

Mix well together. Then stuff the mixture into sausage
casings. These may be of thoroughly washed sheep or hog
intestines, which may be impractical or unavailable, or 25
millimeter artificial casings. Tie them into lengths and
sizes that suit you and hang the uncured sausages for 10
hours in a warm, humid place (about 90 degrees Farenheit). Then raise the temperature with a dry, non-resinous
wood fire, to about 115 degrees Farenheit for 4 hours.

Now smother the fire with sawdust or other green wood
mulch to provide a dense smoke. Keep this on the sausages
for 2 more hours. Savory woods can be used to provide an
aromatic smoke, but this is not essential. Use your own
judgment about this. Let the fire die down after the smok-

ing and ventilate the sausages well. When they have been dried for another day, they will be quite stable and ready for storage and eating. They will be tasty.

⟆ BEANS

Beans, since history began, have been the poor man's meat—his essential protein to run his mind and help his body to be strong.

They are not perfect foods—really—lacking some of the vital protein clusters. But if you have some beans, a few goats, some skinny chickens, and a fish now and then, you can make it.

Millions of the finest peoples of this world have lived this way, producing giants in human compassion, the arts and with a toughened ability to live and create—come what may.

The nutritionists say we need about 70 grams of protein each day. Twenty of these should come from high quality sources such as meats, milk, eggs, fish and certain vegetable sources—notably beans, peas and lentils. When at least a few of these more complex protein clusters are at hand, our bodies may put combinations together, like jig-saw puzzles, and make fine people of us, if we will only try.

It is the dry seed—the bean or pea—that counts, being almost as good as meat. But beans, like potatoes, are variable.

Beans, as far as we know, were first cultivated by Indians of South America. They were of the kidney bean group, which includes the red kidney beans, the mottled pinto ones, and our white navy beans. The limas, soybeans and Asiatic mung beans are of other families. Ours are the American beans. Without them all Mexicans would have died centuries ago—or at least never produced Benito Juarez, Francisco Madero, Orozco, Diego Riviera, Cardenas, or that fine rascal—Pancho Villa.

These men, and all of the people who loved and followed them, were literally . . . full of beans.

The ecological adjustments are quite good with beans. They obey the sun, and follow its light-days in their life schedules. The Montana Great Northerns and the Idaho Reds are wonderful for these areas, but don't yield profitable crops in other places. It is a sunlight thing. The sun tells the bean plant when to grow fast, make blossoms, produce beans, and then die. Further south, the sun talks Spanish to Mexican beans, saying, "*Vámanos frijolitos cultívanse.*"

Beans are like cats. They ignore the farmer's offers of too much care and feeding. They have their own system of using friendly bacteria on their roots to gather foods for them. And—like cats—they will accept some foods greedily, but also thrive on thin diet.

All of this makes beans one of the second greatest foods of all. They will live near you and feed you, no matter where or how you may live.

Granted their goodness, how should we improve and eat them?

We do it differently, by national regions. In New England, we sweeten them, and add pork, onion and mustard. Down the coast, they increase the onion and add tomatoes. In the southwest, beans are treated with meat fats and hot peppers, boiled and "re-fried," when mashed and heated in oil.

The beans, in deep Dixie South, compete with black-eyed peas partly because the easy-going black-eyes will grow almost anywhere. They do well in soils that are thin in lime—and other foods—where most other legumes would die. Happily, they grow nice starchy pea-beans—but don't count on them for either protein or calcium as you would the Great Northerns. But oh how fine they taste when boiled with fat pork or pig knuckles!

Our way to cook Great Northerns, or other good quality beans, goes something like:

Soak a pound of dried beans overnight.

Recognize that the Maine people have the right idea about adding an onion, but chop it up well and mix it with the drained beans. That bit of onion will add to the finest left-over—a cold bean sandwich.

Put the drained soaked beans and onion in a pot with some water and boil until the beans are barely soft enough to chew—about 2 hours.

Use your slotted spoon to transfer the beans to another pot, larding the layers with sliced salt pork, or adding other cured pork. Save the juice.

Put ¼ cup of brown sugar, 4 teaspoons of dry mustard, ¼ cup of dark molasses and ½ cup of water in a mixing bowl. Stir these together, and let stand for about 10 minutes so the mustard can develop its personality.

Mix this with the beans, and add enough of the water in which the beans were cooked to cover the contents of the pot.

Top the pot with a nice chunk of pork, and finish filling with more bean liquor. Then put into a slow oven—250 degrees Farenheit.

Remember the pot six hours later. Lift the lid, spoon out a few beans and blow them cool. Taste for salt and add some if needed. Finish the cooking, uncovered, for half an hour at 300 degrees.

Don't serve these delicious salty fat things to heart patients, or aviators.

Oh, the glorious bean! His salt-sweet juice is like a fine

liqueur, but like his personality, tantalizingly insufficient. You dip, and sip, and have some more. Enchanting— almost. Satiating—almost. Perfect—almost.

That is the bean. The world's most almost food.

✌ BAGELS

The story of bagels is given here because it is a hilarious saga, as well as a tribute to a fine ethnic food that has come down through the centuries.

A bagel, as nearly everyone knows, is a hard, doughnut-like thing that you may slice or break and eat with cream cheese or lox, buttered or plain. In Jewish cuisine, the bagel is a favored bread for breakfast, especially on Sunday mornings.

The rumble about where bagels came from evidently was started when the El Al Israel Airlines published a booklet entitled *El Al Looks Into The Bagel.* This report stated that bagels originated about 1680 when the Turks briefly took Vienna, but were soon driven out again with the assistance of the Poles.

The Turks, according to this report, left behind some sacks of coffee beans which the Viennese thought were camel feed. A Pole who happened to be there, however, knew it was coffee. He got the coffee supply and used it to start Vienna's first coffee house. The bread he served with the coffee was a half-moon shaped morsel called a *kipfel.*

The king of Poland visited Vienna soon thereafter. The people were so grateful for his help in driving out the Turks that they clung to the stirrups of his horse. The Polish kipfel maker was so impressed by this that he changed the shape of his bread to a round shape, like a stirrup, which in German is called a buegel.

This account, which was reported in the *Saturday Review* on November 21, 1964, "To Bagelville and Beyond," set off an explosion of correspondence to the editor that may or may not clarify the history of the insouciant bagel. We will quote tidbits of this correspondence with *Saturday Review's* editor.

First ". . . the informants at El Al . . . are repeating a story that is—to use the local idiom—pure 'Schmoarr'n' (*i.e.*, a flour and sugar omelet dessert). Kolschitzky, the alleged 'Pole,' was probably . . . a Serb, and he surely did not open the first coffeehouse . . . At this time, moreover, there were few if any Jews around, a major expulsion having taken place a decade before the Ottoman attack. In short, the tale is the Austrian, and perhaps also the Yiddish equivalent of George Washington and the cherry tree."

Saturday Review, December 12, 1964
Thomas M. Barker
Associate Professor of History
State University of New York
Albany

Then ". . . The true development of the bagel is related in the Bible, 1 Samuel 25:18, *et seq.*, where David's amatory excursions are discussed. It is there stated, in part: 'Then Abigail made haste, and took two hundred loaves . . . and laid them on asses.' Obviously, during the ride through the desert on the bony and lumpy backs of asses, the loaves assumed their now well-known shape and consistency. It needs no imagination to recognize the perversion of her name as well as her character. 'Abigail' became 'Bigail,' which was quickly corrupted to 'bagel.'

"The unfair attempt . . . to deprive us Jews of the credit for this ancient gastronomic horror must be nipped in the bud."

Saturday Review, January 16, 1965
Thomas L. Parsonnet
Newark, New Jersey

And then ". . . Horace Sutton's article about bagels . . . is excellent. I am sure he will be pleased to learn the facts concerning the discovery of bagel.

"In 381 B.C., in Crete, there lived a baker named Bagelus. Now, Bagelus had gout. At that time, the standard remedy for gout . . . was to encase the large toe in warm dough. One day Bagelus was basking in the hot sun, his feet propped up, in order to give his dough-ringed toes the full benefit of the heat. It was an unusually hot day in Crete. In fact, Cleides tells us . . . that the temperature on that particular day reach 117 degrees. The dough on Bagelus's toes hardened. When he awakened, he discovered on his toes a fully formed and hardened formation of large brown rings. . . . all the animals in the neighborhood, attracted by the odor, where now pressing in upon him, trying to eat the rings off his feet. Bagelus removed the baked ringlet from his left foot, sniffed at it, then bit into it, experiencing a most delectable and irrestible taste sensation.

. . . .

"It is true that the bagel has been appreciated and developed mainly in Jewish cooking; but now that the bagel is becoming universalized, it may be well to set the matter straight concerning its historical origin in ancient Greece."

> *Saturday Review*, December 26, 1964
> Cull Pepper
> Visiting Professor of Ancient Mores
> University of Athens
> Athens, Greece

Then ". . . it was not the bagel that Bagelus discovered, but the doughnut.

". . . the bagel was introduced into Crete by King Solomon and the king of Phoenicia. It was an immediate success, and it was only after Bagelus discovered the doughnut that its popularity as a breakfast food was somewhat diminished. This in part was due to the fact that the bagel was at this time made in the form of a square. It was only much later that the Greek mathematician Archimedes . . . suggested that the bagel should be made round.

". . . there remains a hard core of bagel devotees who claim that the rich succulence of the bagel can be savored only when it is in the shape of a square.

"The famous singing commercial, 'A Kauffman Square Bagel can't roll off your table' is well known throughout the Middle East."

> *Saturday Review,* January 16, 1965
> Mendel Trubnick
> Algernon Professor of Semitic Semantics
> Queens College, Flushing, New York

And finally this touching note ". . . would it interest any to learn that my life was once saved by a bagel? It happened in the Korean War. My dear sweet mother had sent me a box of goodies . . . among which were six bagels. I stuffed them into various pockets of my overcoat. . . . We were given the assignment of wiping an enemy guerilla operation five miles north of our position. . . . we ran into enemy machinegun activity. I was hit in three places. Miraculously, each place was protected by a bagel and my life was saved. The doctors said the adamantine hardness of the bagel . . . resisted the force of the bullets."

> *Saturday Review,* February 20, 1965
> Bailey Richards
> Chicago, Illinois

There you have it. Did Bagelus, after all, invent bagels? And what are those mischievous Greeks up to, anyway? For our part, we suspect bagels were invented in New York in 1893 by Zhelleck P. Bagel.

Many people are unaware that bagels are both boiled and baked when they are properly made. The following is a good recipe, adapted from *The World Of Breads* by Delores Casella, David White Co., New York. 1966:

3 cups of whole grain flour	⅔ cup of warm potato
1 teaspoon of salt	water (from boiling a
4 tablespoons of sugar	couple of potatoes)

1 cake of yeast	3 tablespoons of cooking oil
	2 eggs
	4 quarts of boiling water

Mix the flour, salt and half of the sugar in a mixing bowl. Dissolve the yeast in the potato water, and add it to the flour mixture. Then add the oil and stir. Beat the eggs with a fork. Add them and stir until the dough forms a ball.

Put the ball of dough on a floured board and knead thoroughly for 5 minutes. Then, put it into a buttered bowl, cover, and let rise until the dough is doubled. Punch down, and let rise again. Punch down again. Put on the floured board and knead again, until the dough is smooth.

Divide the dough into 12 or 15 portions, and form each into a strip about 6 inches long and ¾ inch thick. Form a ring with each strip, and pinch the ends together. Do not try to cut with a doughnut cutter.

Add the remaining 2 tablespoons of sugar to the boiling water. Drop the bagel rings into the water, one at a time, cooking 4 or 5 at once. Simmer them for 5 or 6 minutes after they rise to the surface of the water. Then, lift them out of the water with a long handled fork, and place them on a lightly greased cookie sheet. Cool for about 5 minutes. Then bake in a 375 degree oven for about 30 minutes, or until the crust is golden brown and crisp.

❧ SOUL FOODS

The U.S. slaves did not bring corn bread and chitlins here with them from Africa, like lunch on a safari. Their homeland customs were smashed. A curtain fell behind them. They had to build a whole new food system under duress in a new place. Two hundred years later we called it soul food.

This part of Americana is more substantial than usually thought. It certainly is more than a Wings n' Things palace in a ghetto, or Daddy Grace's Kitchen where white folk can slum around and say at the office next day, "Hey man! We found this little place and jeez, they got real soul food, chitlins and beans and collards and things. But it's dangerous, you know." Back of all of this is 200 years of black investments in how to live on corn and greens and the spare parts of pigs on 10¢ a day.

The ancestors of present-day soul foods were corn meal and pork. Plantation customs required the planter to provide each slave with about 20 pounds of meal and 3 pounds of pork a week. Fredrick Olmstead, an eminent New England farmer and merchant, reported in 1856, in *A Journey In the Seaboard Slave States:*

"The general allowance of food was thought to be a peck and a half of meal and three pounds of bacon a week. This, it was observed, was as much meal as they could eat, but they would be glad to have more bacon, sometimes they receive four pounds, but it is oftener that they get less than three. It is distributed to them on Saturday nights; or, in the better managed plantations, sometimes on Wednesdays, to prevent their using it extravagantly, or selling it for whiskey on Sunday. This distribution is called a 'drawing' and is made by the overseer to all the heads of families or single negroes. Except on the smallest plantations, where cooking is done in the house of the proprietor, there is a cook-house, furnished with a large copper for boiling, and an oven. Every night the negroes take their 'mess,' for the next day's breakfast and dinner, to the cook, to be prepared for the next day. Custom varies as to the time it is served out to them; sometimes at morning and noon, at other times at noon and night. Each negro marks his meat by cuts, so that he shall know it from the rest, and

153

they observe each other's rights with regard to this, punctiliously."

Some state laws regulated the food rations of slaves. The laws of Louisiana, for example, required the planters to give each slave 200 pounds of pork a year, which would be nearly 4 pounds a week.

The corn meal and pork, in a typical situation, were supplemented with the crops of the country-side such as greens from the fields and fence-rows, a patch of turnips and other vegetables, fish, turtles, squirrels, rabbits, possum and raccoons, chitlins, pigs feet, heads, skins and tails, wild apples, grapes and berries and grains.

The greens went into the big pot with the spare parts of the pork, and that kind of soul food was born, collards, mustard, kale and turnip greens, with fat and a bit of protein from the pork.

Butchering day was a time for the mammas to save. The hog's heads came home, where they were washed, scalded, split, cleaned and made into head cheese, ears and all. Some of the meat was mixed with meal to make scrapple, combining the meat and cereal to make a whole food. The pig's feet were brined and saved for another day.

The grease can on the stove caught the pig and poultry grease which went into the corn bread and greens, for calories and flavor. It moved into the cities with black folk, during their migrations, and fed thousands who died too soon. This, too, was soul food.

The practices of soul food cooking are sustained, however, by the multi-generation black families who gather on Sundays, holidays, weddings and funerals. These families are clusters of strength in America. They are thrifty, conservative, peace-loving and vital.

Nana cooks on Sundays. Eight or ten satellite families of sons, daughters, aunts, uncles, cousins and grandmas know she does, and they come in random fashion, some after church, others later, some this Sunday, some next, and so on. There is always enough no matter who comes by. They go straight to the kitchen, peek into the big pots, and say, "Oh, collards," or "Oh, turkey wings," or "Oh, lima beans," and if they want some, they eat. Big Daddy strolls around and helps everyone to find places to sit or he takes a nap. It is not unusual, in the midst of all of this, for a daughter to say, "I'm going home to eat my spare ribs." She has been cooking, too, and her own food is on her mind. This communal eating of much-loved foods in the family clans of black folk today is the remnant custom from plantation eating 200 years ago, when the slaves brought their corn meal, meat, greens, and other things to the big pots and cooked their meals together.

Soul food is a sturdy diet. Here are a few recipes.

COLLARD GREENS FOR 6 PEOPLE

Buy or gather 3 pounds of collard greens. Wash and trim them. Also, get 2 smoked ham hocks, or a piece of salt pork, or a "streak of lean." This is soul language for a fairly fat piece of bacon.

Put the meat in a 6 quart pot, in 2 quarts of water, and boil it for 1½ hours. Add the greens and a teaspoon of salt. Also add 8 or 10 shakes out of a red pepper can, ¼ teaspoon of red pepper. Boil for another 1½ hours, when the greens should be tender. Serve with corn bread, spare ribs, a chicken, ham, or turkey wings.

These features of this recipe are noteworthy: Most black folk couldn't care less whether it is organic. Cooking things a long time is customary and red pepper is used when boiling things, black pepper for the frying and roasting.

NATURAL CORN BREAD

Get some real white corn meal, stone ground with the germs still in the corn. (If local supplies fail, you can get this from The Infinity Company, 84 McDougal Street, New York, 10012. They operate a stone mill in the heart of New York City.)

Put 2½ cups of the meal in a mixing bowl. Then add:

> 2½ teaspoons of baking powder
> 1 teaspoon of salt
> 3 tablespoons of shortening (a good cooking oil may be used)
> 1 cup of milk

Mix it all together. If you like it thinner, add water. Put it into a greased pan, and bake at 450 degrees in the oven until it is brown (20 or 25 minutes).

The old recipes permit adding pork grease and also pork cracklings, crisp baked skins of pigs. Such corn bread, 2 inches thick and loaded with grease and cracklings, is for hard working people who need 4,000 calories a day.

STRING BEANS WITH POTATOES

Buy or gather 2 pounds of old-fashioned Kentucky Wonder string beans or other old-style substantial string beans. Wash, string and snap them. Also, get 2 smoked ham hocks or half a pound of ham. Put the meat and the snapped beans in a big pot. Add ½ teaspoon of salt, some red pepper, and a medium onion. Boil for 2 hours.

Meantime, peel 4 fairly large white potatoes, and cut them to cooking size. Add these to the beans after they have cooked for 2 hours. Cover again and boil for 20 minutes, or until the potatoes are done. Then add a tablespoon of butter and a good sprinkle of black pepper. Cover again and simmer for 5 minutes before serving.

These soul food cooks did not worry about losing the vitamins through over-cooking. Their aim was to get tough things tender, and be sure everything was well done.

* * *

As our country grows, with 200 million people now and 400 million with our grandchildren, T-bone steaks will be rare no matter how they are cooked. They will be found only in gourmet restaurants that have Roy Rogers statues outside.

The basic ideas of soul foods and other diversified dishes will have a major place in such an improvement. We will boil as well as fry, and we will surely save the good juices. The grease pot of the rural South will be replaced with the stock pot, and good soups will flourish. They will resemble the Latin American *sopa*, which is big, thick, rich, and a whole meal in itself. You order chicken soup, *sopa de pollo*, and it comes with half a chicken in it.

Our road is turning, and more people are travelling our way. The kitchens will be serving rich soups and boiled things. Some travellers, however, will just keep moving. They'll be the ones with crunchy granola in their shoulder bags.

CHAPTER TEN

Putting It All Together in a Good Food Community

A NEWSPAPER advertised, during a recent weekend, the sale of poultry fryers by a leading supermarket for 33¢ a pound. We knew the district directors of this supermarket chain, so we called the chief of the poultry department and said, "We've noticed your sale of broilers for 33¢ a pound, and we've been studying these things. That's a pretty low price. What would your normal price be if there was no special sale?"

"Oh, 38¢," he said.

"We noticed that the average wholesale price for dressed chickens in trucklots is 30¢," we said, "that leaves you only 3¢ a pound, or 9%, as a retailer's margin. Pretty low."

"It is lower than that," he said, "we buy these in a special pack ready to put in the show case. We paid 31¢ for those birds. We never make any money on the weekend sales. It's a leader."

"Well," we said, "Katz's Kosher Supermarket had their fine dressed poultry, as usual, for 49¢ a pound and you had to fight to get in line to buy some. That's 16¢ more than your sale price, and 11¢ over the regular market. How do they keep their customers coming at that high price?"

"Oh, that's kosher poultry," he said, "it's the choice of the flocks with a rabbi's blessing."

"But half of the people buying those chickens were just ordinary customers, looking for a good frying chicken," we said, "they used to be your customers. Why don't you start selling good chickens again?"

"I've thought of that," he replied, "but I don't know where I'd get them anymore. All I can get are U.S. number 1's."

We checked out the high quality kosher birds. They came from a farming community in eastern Pennsylvania, where they were raised under contracts by a big kosher processor-supplier. He specified, in the production contracts, the feeding of the birds and a severe limit on the drugs and growth stimulants that could be used in their production. The base price to contract growers was from 2¢ to 3¢ higher than the prevailing farm price. He paid 17¢ to 18¢ a pound when the prevailing price was 15¢. These contracts, which prevented a debasing of the birds in their production, was the basis for this flow of better poultry into our markets.

Such business arrangements are available to all food retailers in the U.S. who wish to serve their quality-minded customers and help to stop the downhill skid in the quality of all classes of food products. We have a dynamic business system, however, in which changes occur in a follow-the-leader fashion. Let us visualize this by describing the models of two food communities in which vital changes were made, one in an established metropolitan area and the other in a new setting. We shall call these the Meadowdale and Nucla communities.

MEADOWDALE—VITAL IMPROVEMENTS IN AN URBAN AREA

Meadowdale is an old city with new suburban edges. It

159

has become, since 1950, a megalopolis of 2 million people. About 22% of these are black and 78% are white, near the national ratio. If you carved out the center of Meadowdale, however, you would find this part to be 85% black, a concentrated subculture within the larger city.

Meadowdale was served in 1971 by 3 national food chains, 2 regional supermarket companies, a strong consumers' co-op with 16 supermarket units, 37 health and organic food stores, 18 large ethnic and specialty food markets, and dozens of convenience stores. The city's food products moved into these various places in steady streams from farms, canneries, freezing plants, processors, food factories and importing places at the seaport cities. The small independent stores could not do much to change these food streams or create new ones. This role was reserved for the big supermarkets and co-operative organizations who bought in carlots, trucklots and trainloads. They governed the good trends and the other stores had to follow.

The food business in Meadowdale in 1971 was in a state of flux. The customers were restless. Prices were still rising. The news stories about mercury in fish, contaminated chickens, DDT in the vegetables, and poisoned vichyssoise soup were undermining the confidence of everyone, even the clerks and check-out girls. Many customers were turning to the kosher markets for better meats and to the health food stores for organic produce. Meadowdale, tired of war, taxes, traffic, high prices, crime and smog, was also grumbling about its food.

The black people of the subcommunity, within this fretful scene, had a new problem. The big chain stores and supermarkets were moving out of the inner city. They could not make money in this non-typical ethnic market with their computerized inventory controls and management systems. They retreated to the suburbs and affluent neighborhoods where the computers understood the language and the big food trucks could roll, handling mostly white folk's food.

Such was the situation in Meadowdale in 1971. By 1975, hypothetically, many vital improvements had been made. The big consumers' co-op, with its 60,000 members and 16 modern stores, served as the trigger force to precipitate these changes. The members demanded safer, better foods. The management responded with moves that were perilous from a conventional business standpoint, but possible in a co-operative organization that had a built-in community of support. The management made these moves: It eliminated the dead-level U.S. number 1 poultry from all of the stores and replaced it with certified, safe poultry from a dependable contract supplier. These birds were raised on a wholesome feeding program that omitted growth drugs and arsenic. The retail price was raised 5¢ a pound to cover the costs of the adequately fed poultry and to commence a waste recycling operation that was undertaken by the poultry grower.

The president of the co-op said, in announcing this move, "We are taking this step in our role of serving the civic as well as business interests of our members. Someone must do it, to halt the down-grading of our foods. We will do it. We are removing the unsafe, lower priced poultry from all of our stores, since it is uneconomical to carry both grades and further, our members do not wish for us to temporize any longer with foods of questionable safety and quality."

The co-op had withdrawal pains. Many of its dollar-minded members went to other markets for cheaper poultry. This adverse trend was soon cured, however, when 15,000 new members joined the co-op to support its good food leadership in Meadowdale.

The poultry experience encouraged this food co-op to take a stand on beef and stilbestrol, a synthetic female hormone growth stimulant. It appointed a capable work group, headed by an eminent biochemist, to study the problem, to equip the co-op's management with accurate up-to-date information and a recommendation. The work group reported that the world research situation was clouded. The long run effects of stilbestrol used in meat production, on humans that ate the meat, were still unknown, but were dubious as indicated by adverse effects on research animals, such as rats and mice. The work group recommended that the co-op offer stilbestrol-free meat, as a free choice alternative, to its customers, along with the up-to-date information. The management adopted the recommendation and put clearly labelled stocks of normally grown beef, free of stilbestrol, in all of its stores. The average price for all cuts of this meat was 8¢ a pound higher than for the regular beef.

The demand for the safer, better beef began rising about 10% a month, however, despite the higher price.

This co-op's management decided to help in compensating for the rise in beef costs by offering a high grade of soyaburger, made under contract by a reliable meat company. This product had 16% protein, of which 60% was derived from vegetable materials, mainly from soy beans. It was offered to customers, along with clear labelling and a technical information and recipe leaflet, at 75¢ a pound. It was an immediate commercial success.

The co-op put in generous stocks of certified vegetables and fruits, in special display counters in all of the stores, so customers might have choices between these labelled products and conventional produce. Organic fruits and vegetables were included, when good and reliable supplies could be obtained. When they were offered, they were certified as organic.

The citrus displays featured certified oranges and orange juice, with a guaranteed minimum of vitamin C (ascorbic acid) and specified sugar-acid and total solids readings. A relative freedom from chlorinated hydrocarbon materials (such as DDT) and other economic poisons, was also assured. These nutritional and food safety factors were covered in the supplier's certificate, which was displayed at the point of each sale.

The cop-op found that safe, high quality non-organic fruits and vegetables, produced under reliable contracts, cost about 10% more than the conventional goods, and that the fully organic produce was about 40% higher when it was available without expensive air shipments. The lesser quantities, in each case, contributed to the higher costs.

VEGELAC—A MILK-LIKE FLUID FOR PEOPLE

This co-operative decided to offer vegelac, a high nutritional milk-like beverage, as a move to help its members in dealing with their milk price and supply problems. It was a bold move, almost like rejecting the flag and motherhood, and nearly unseated the board of directors and the management. The vegelac won a place in the market and brought new customers, however, and this move, although a bit ahead of its time, was finally vindicated.

The new product, vegelac, was formulated by a capable food research center and made by a nearby milk company. It had a whole milk base and non-fat milk ingredients, and derived its uniformity and lower price from high quality vegetable materials. According to all known tests, this milk-like product was fully as good for human use as conventional whole milk. Its inherent costs were substantially lower, so it could be consumed by more people. The retail price was 25¢ a quart and 45¢ a half gallon.

THE CHAIN REACTIONS

These various moves of Meadowdale's consumer co-op were sufficient to generate chain reactions throughout the food community. Organic and certified food displays soon appeared in most supermarkets. Stores that did not follow the new trends found their sales lagging. The new vegelac moved into milk sections all over the city. Soyaburger found its way into the meat displays, and then into Meadowdale's restaurants and hamburger palaces. It won the young peoples' vote because it was juicier, better and cheaper than the old stuff.

The Food and Drug Administration of this age then reacted in a bizzare fashion by seizing the first stocks of certified and rated oranges, on the basis that they reflected upon the quality and safety of untested oranges, which might have equal quality and safety and therefore were improperly labelled. FDA of that time said, "Who knows? Perhaps part of all of those other oranges are equally good, even better."

An organized consumer group from Meadowdale intervened with a successful court action, freeing the oranges, showing that testing and certifying, per se, added values to the products, and made them different and better from the consumer's standpoint.

An organic supermarket that hung up a sign saying: "These Chickens Contain No Arsenic" was compelled to take it down, however, since it implied that other chickens in the market did contain arsenic, which the FDA said was unfair, even if they did. Subsequently the U.S. Department of Agriculture of the time was pressured into withdrawing its sanction for use of arsenicals as growth stimulants in poultry production.

Meadowdale was not alone in its good food actions. It was joined by cities and people all over the country. The Congress of 1976, in response to all of this marketplace activity, passed the Food Quality and Environmental Act, setting up legal mechanisms for food quality controls and for waste recycling in the food industry, using the aforementioned basic principles. It also passed the Inner City Food Distribution Act, which diverted 200 million dollars of USDA allotted funds for use in financing modern food retailing enterprises in inner city areas. The counterparts of Safeway, A&P, Grand Union, Acme, Tradewell and Giant Food conceded that America's minority peoples, black, Mexican American, Indian and Puerto Rican, should have supermarket services, with computers that talked the inner city languages. They supported this essential legislation.

An amendment to the General Services and Procurement Act was made in 1977, providing that federal purchases of basic foods could be made only from firms whose production was governed by Food Quality and Environmental Protection Orders.

These broad public actions by Congress were signals that America was unified in its drives to become a clean and well fed nation again. They were echoes from a hundred Meadowdales in all parts of the country.

We, as practical food revolutionists, should know the paths of progress indicated by the hypothetical but strong consumer reaction in Meadowdale, by the votes by Congress and the subsequent redirection of national food and environmental policies. These are the steps and Meadow-

165

dale is an illustration of what has to happen in the cities
and neighborhoods throughout the country. An organized
consumers' force must be mobilized, and then it must act.
In our illustration, it was the consumers' co-operative. It
could, however, have been a large buying club, a labor
union dealing with a supermarket chain, or a big PTA
organization. The point is that private business in the U.S.
will seldom act in behalf of consumers except when it is
strongly pressured to do so by the customers. The action
by the consumers must be timely. It must be aimed at conditions that everyone, including the food companies,
knows must be improved. A chain reaction can then be
generated using the nature of the U.S. business system. Its
equilibrium is delicate and nervous, although always unan-
imous in effect, whether in deciding that cars should have
fins or no fins, that gasoline should be 39¢ or 37¢ a gallon,
if there should be two movies on airplane trips or no
movies, etc. Even small changes cause immediate study
and responses among the big competitors. In the case of
foods, they know you are dissatisfied. They are awaiting
your signals, hoping you will not ask for too much change.
The Meadowdale co-op's action can compel similar actions by other stores and markets, lest they lose customers.
The chain reaction can go clear across the country. We
are a nation, in which Bellingham, Washington gets pneu-
monia when Miami, Florida sneezes. Changes are contagious in all of the cities and neighborhoods, since they
are almost all part of one U.S. national market, watching
one TV program. When Meadowdale gets certified safe
chickens in its supermarkets, therefore, St. Louis will have
some too. That is the way our country works. The food
industry must have incentives to act, prices, patronage,
profits. Otherwise it cannot and will not act, even if life

and death are at stake. A true business man will perish in his own smog, and weep while his children choke and die, unless he is paid to cut down those deadly gasses. This, again, is the way our system works. In the case of Meadowdale, the business incentives were the additional 5¢ a pound for the good, safe poultry, and more customers. Even a co-operative has to have enough income to pay its expenses. The responses of government, by Congress and the food agencies, come last. These are political institutions that mirror national trends, rather than create them. They are followers, not leaders. The dynamics of American life are in the private sector.

These are the reasons why consumers should find ways to influence the markets, to influence the food companies and make them bring in better stocks of food, using their buying power as a leverage. Such actions build and shape consumers as a political and legislative force. It is only then that Congress will pass essential legislation and redirect the policies of its food agencies. That is the way our system works. Congress speaks last, proudly saying, "Look what we did!"

NUCLA—A NEW FOOD COMMUNITY

Nucla is an imaginary place, because it isn't built yet. It will be built soon, however, in a hundred places, because the country needs it. Our young people probing for homesteads and for organic farming communes are searching for Nucla, so we will describe it to assist the planners of this good food community, some of whom may be you and your children.

This Nucla will be located on one of those pieces of land you see so often these days, where the old fields are half-tended, the old farmhouses are nearly forgotten, the school districts have collapsed, and the old towns are nearly gone, all because the people went away to the big cities. We shall build Nucla on 100,000 acres of this underused rural land.

"First," you may ask, "is it really good land? Would it be underused and rundown if it were really good land?"

Let us answer: Most non-mountainous land in the U.S. is good for use in some kind of food, fiber, animal or timber production. We have crippled many of these opportunities, however, with a competitive business system that harshly eliminates medium class lands and medium class producers. If your use of land is only 1% below par, in raising tomatoes for example, you usually will go out of business. This austere situation, which is related to over-specialization and the development of monocultures killed tomato farming in many states that had grown good tomato crops for many years. Their growers were knocked out by cheap factory-type production in California, Florida, Texas and Mexico.

The desperate balance among competing producers, and then the imbalance that puts many of them out of business, is a challenge that we should face. We should find ways to relax the tensions and open opportunities in medium grade areas for medium grade people.

The land, in the case of Nucla, is good enough. It is near a medium sized city, three hills over. Ten thousands acres of the hundred thousand is grade number 1 soil, although requiring some clearing and drainage; 20,000 acres is number 2 soil, suitable for high class uses after improvement with modernized organic farming; 40,000 acres is of number 3 soil, good for corn, potatoes, grain, hay and pasture, when improved with organic farming; 30,000 acres is precious woodland and wildlife in which it would be sinful

168

to turn the soil or try to grow a crop. That would disturb the rabbits, wild turkeys and chickadees.

We have had experience in converting number 4 land, rocky, sterile soil, into number 2 land, by building organic life into it and harnessing the forces of nature. The farmers of Nucla can do the same. The following guides and principles are paramount: Nucla will be a closed system community. This means that its wastes will be processed and re-used in the economy. The (a) human, (b) animal and agricultural, and (c) processing and industrial wastes will be processed and cycled back into further production. Nucla will be diversified in its agriculture and in its economy. It will include human, civic and long range factors in its feasibility analyses. The people of Nucla will ask, "What can we produce here to employ our people and to use the resources of Nature?" rather than, "What can we buy a little cheaper from California and Texas, since they are mixing their soils and exploiting their agricultural workers?" Nucla will be significantly self-sufficient because of its diversified economy and it will process its own products, within the reasonable limits of practicality, for its own markets. It will try to serve itself with many of the basic food products, such as bread, meats, poultry, vegetables, fruits, grains, milk and cheese because it feels the U.S. system of over specialization and long distance supplying of foods is debasing their quality and safety, and creating excessive financial and social stresses in our society. Nucla will use old skills and wisdom in its farming and food enterprises. It will, for example, mingle and rotate the crops to sustain fertility and to control insects and plant diseases. Nucla will also use, however, advanced scientific knowledge and the technologies of our time in producing the food products and in processing the organic wastes. It will, for example, capture and use the methane

169

gas from its sewage as an energy source, and it will convert its sludge and compost into ultra-modern, balanced fertilizers to save on money and labor.

Nucla will seek a full use and re-use of its water and the conservation of its water supplies. The historical evidence shows that water conservation has been possible in all human communities that tried to achieve it even in earlier times when cisterns, catch basins, water lifts, conduits and small reservoirs were used. Nucla will emulate these wise ancestors.

Nucla will count its young people as its most valuable resource and its economy as the best facility for their life-long education. This concept widens Nucla's spectrum of business feasibility. Even marginal enterprises will be included in the economy if they don't cost too much and if they enrich the lives of the young, and widen their vocational opportunities. Nucla may, accordingly, engage in producing mushrooms, beer, rare cheeses, truffles, horse-radish, riding horses, pickled nuts and fine hardwood furniture.

Let us try to reflect such guides in a physical design for the Nucla good food community.

THE DESIGN OF NUCLA

A hundred thousand acres is a rectangular area about 10 by 16 miles. This makes 160 square miles of 640 acres each. The climate here is moderate: 32 inches of rainfall and a seven-month growing season. The land area has two rivers and eight main tributaries. Water is consequently available for the seasonal irrigation of 15,000 crop acres.

We shall divide the land, for planning and illustrating purposes, into a Euclidian square, with 10 main utilization areas thusly:

THE NUCLA COMMUNITY

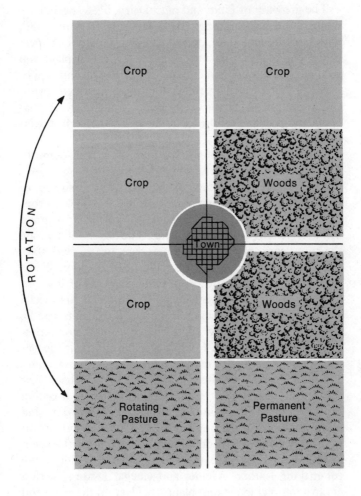

The town should be centrally located with a belt of land around it for perennial suburban uses, such as:

The growing of fruits and nuts. Dairy, beef, sheep, hog, poultry and horse raising. A cannery and freezing plant, with packing, cold storage and shipping facilities. A meat processing plant. A bakery. A grain processing plant and feed mills. A lumber and building materials mill and supply yard. A winery and brewery. A sewage treatment plant. Composting and fertilizer production facilities. A machine and transport shops. Warehouses and freight terminals.

The main roads, topography permitting, can come to Nucla's center and coverage in its beltway.

The production system of Nucla, while designed to yield abundant, and increasing, quantities of basic crops and goods, will encourage a successful nurturing of good income-yielding special enterprises. The basics will include the root crops, grain, corn, hay, forage, beans, vegetables and truck crops, nuts, fruits, milk, beef, poultry, sheep, hogs, bees, pasture and horses. Other features of interest, however, may be: An advanced development in special and gourmet sausages, scrapple, corned beef, hams, bacon, cheeses, highest quality eggs, cut chickens, frozen pre-cooked meats, and wild fowl. Vegetable and fruit specialties, including soups, jams and jellies, honey, mushrooms, and field ripened produce. Excellent wine and beer, featuring full malt ales, bitter and stout. Fine horse breeding and production for riding and racing, with boarding and rental services. Mushroom caves as a year-round operation using the horse bedding and manure, with the spent materials then going to the compost piles. A hide house for making leather. A cider and vinegar factory, with a companion pickle making plant, ancillary to the wine and beer enterprises. They will all use the same scientists and laboratories. A travel and recreation service, with good city connection.

Skilled farm planners and ecologists will put the crops and fields into rotation that reduces pests and agricultural diseases, and thereby reduces the need for poisonous sprays. They may decide, for example, that the potatoes should follow the pasture, to avoid a build-up of potato scab, wire-worms and bugs; or that the grain should follow the potatoes, to vary the ecological cycle and change the plant residues. They might decide that the beans and other legumes called dicotyledonous plants because their seeds can be snapped open to reveal two separate and complete halves, should follow the monocots such as corn, which may have many individual seeds, but where each seed is one complete unit, thus again breaking the food chains for the crop pests, using nature's control methods. They might feel that the corn and milo, a grain like millet, should come next, again alternating the classes of plants, that vegetable and truck crops should then follow, to clean up the accumulated fertility from previous fertilizations, and then that the land should go into pasture again to renew the soil with the presence and droppings of livestock.

The fields may be many, and there will be numerous farmers. Still the mixed farming techniques will be used in the economy of Nucla, by plan and by contract agreements. It is too expensive as forty years in America has demonstrated to do it otherwise. The U.S. Department of Agriculture has been paying $3.6 billion a year to buy bad farming and bad food crops. An intelligent use of one-tenth of such public outlays would underwrite the farming for 1,000 Nuclas in the United States.

Earth Foods

The farm and woodlands of Nucla will produce about 10 million dollars of primary agricultural and forestry crops a year. This is new wealth that serves, in any sound rural-urban system, as the basis for other than farm jobs, trade, incomes, new products, more money, services, taxes and wealth. In the case of Nucla's diversified society, which will retain its young people and provide the full range of public services, the 10 million dollars of primary production is the foundation for a 100 million dollar economy. This ten-fold increase is due to: The full processing of the crops and animals into products of highest intrinsic and money value. The spending and re-spending of money. The full development and operation of a wide range of rural non-farm enterprises. The full development and operation of civic services and enterprises, such as schools, medical and dental services, recreation, etc. The devlopment of a parity trading basis in commerce between Nucla and the outside world.

A sound population for Nucla on such an economic base would be about 20,000 people (The 1 trillion dollar economy of the U.S. sustains about 82 million people in the work force. About $12,000 of gross national product transactions make one job. Nucla's 100 million dollars, using such a rough indicator, could support about 8,000 gainfully employed people. About one-half of these people will be full and part time workers, managers, farmers, scientists, artists, craftsmen, tradesmen, business men and women, teachers and service people. The remainder will be the very young, the old and non-working persons. They will comprise about 6,000 families.

Nucla will be a fairly young community, since it is on America's frontier, and frontiers attract the young.

Nucla's 20,000 people will eat about 20 million calories a year and about 500 million grams of protein as well as many fats and minerals. They will produce, as an end result of their eating, large quantities of organic wastes.

NUCLA'S WASTE CYCLING SYSTEM

People are notorious producers of wastes. Animals, when they are kept by people, are even more impressive in their ability to foul up the landscape. Cows, for example, are quite large—a big one may weigh 1,600 pounds. A cow will produce as much odious waste in a day as will be produced by 16 or 18 people. A steer in a feedlot will produce as much organic waste as 10 people. A hog will equal two people, and ten hens will do as much damage, in the sewage department, as one person.

All of which means that the Nucla planners must include the livestock and birds in designing the waste disposal system.

We will base the waste disposal system, for present planning purposes, on the installation of an Imhoff tank and sewage treatment system, with a companion composting and waste treatment operation. The Imhoff facility, described in simplest terms, is only a digestor where trillions of bacteria can conveniently digest organic wastes, reducing them to their simpler forms and chemical structures.

The organic wastes of the entire community will move into this Imhoff unit, carried in liquid suspension through Nucla's sewer lines. Garbage grinders in all kitchens will facilitate a separation of the garbage from the metals, cans

CROSS SECTION OF AN IMHOFF TANK

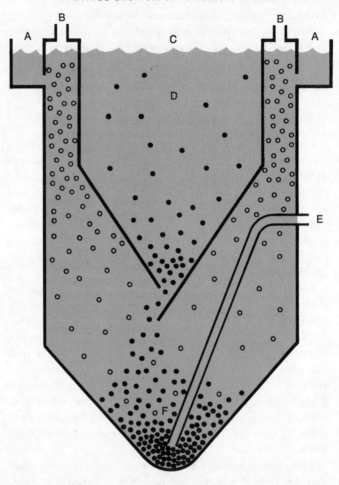

A. Liquid from digestor
B. Gas collector
C. Liquid from settler
D. Settling chamber
E. Sludge pump discharge
F. Digesting sludge

and trash. Everything organic will be picked up in the waterborne collection system, and moved to the Imhoff tank.

The bacterial digestion processes then may occur, reducing long-chain proteins to simpler combinations of amino acids, and the carbohydrates to more elemental forms. There are three classes of end products: water, methane and other gasses, and the solid matter, called sludge. Let us look at each separately.

THE WATER AND GAS EFFLUENT

Nucla cannot afford to waste its sewage water. That would be bad water conservation, and the wasteage could saturate and foul other areas. The water will therefore be treated and reused for agricultural and other purposes. The main use, during summer, will be in the irrigation of crops. This is seasonal, however, and a broader range is needed. The effluent will be piped into an aerating lagoon or reservoir where it will be both aerated and if necessary, treated with oxygen. Experience and tests show that such water, after a cycle of treatment in this manner, is actually superior to the river waters that are commonly used by large U.S. cities for domestic distribution.

In case of water scarcity, all of Nucla's animals and birds can be sustained with the Imhoff effluent, after it has gone through the lagoon processing with oxygen. If further scarcity exists, this water is fully acceptable as the secondary supply for the operation of toilets and sewers and for watering of lawns, parks and flowers.

The decomposition of the cellulose, sugar, and other carbohydrates of sewage by the Imhoff bacteria gives off methane gas, which has energy value. This is the phenomenon recently celebrated in the news, in which an English inventor ran his automobile on chicken manure. This dubious material was being processed by bacteria in the inventor's portable tank, giving off methane gas to run his car.

The Nucla digestor has the capacity, tentatively, to produce about 1,000 kilowatts of electrical energy per hour from the recovery and burning of its methane gas.

THE SEWAGE SLUDGE AND THE COMPOSTING UNIT

Present research indicates that a ureaform treatment of sewage sludge will be practical and feasible without a prior composting of this solid matter from the Imhoff digester. We shall assume, however, that a prior composting of this waste will be advantageous. The sludge will be moved, therefore, directly from the Imhoff facility to the Nucla composting fields, which should be located nearby.

The big compost piles will receive this sludge, and all other bulky organic wastes of the community, the animal and poultry manures, crop wastes, cannery and freezing plant trimmings and refuse, the slaughter wastes, and garbage that missed the Imhoff collection lines. All of this is fuel for the compost piles.

These piles are built in long windrows that can be cheaply turned with machinery. They, too, are bacterial digestion units. The temperature is controlled with additions of water, and by the turning of the piles. Skilled technicians encourage the right kinds of bacteria to do a thorough job. The end product is a rich, sterile compost material, produced in less than 90 days.

Such compost has three uses in the Nucla recycling system: As a soil amendment to enrich the soil and raise its moisture holding capacity. As food for next year's crops, nature's way of fertilizing. As a material for reacting with ureaform, and possibly other materials in making an ultra-modern, organic-based, complete, balanced, pelleted, high analysis fertilizer that can be shipped for hundreds of miles into a wide range of farm and urban markets.

There we have it. All of Nucla's organic wastes can be used and transmuted into money values in its economy.

NUCLA'S TRADING POSITION

Nucla, the good food community, will not produce poor food products. To do so would violate its basic policies and breach its purpose. Also, it would be too expensive to divide the production into good and poor parts. The land will all be fertilized too well. The livestock and poultry will all have balanced diets and be kept in pleasant places. The processing facilities will be adjusted for gentle treatments. No stocks of drugs and additives will be near at hand. The labels will be accurate and complete. It would be too much trouble to fill orders for bad foods.

Nucla will therefore exploit its position as one of America's fine food suppliers providing certified excellent products to anyone who cares to buy.

The present premium on such products in the U.S., in the organic and other markets, is about 40%. Such a trade advantage is sufficient to finance Nucla, to clear and drain its lands, build the Imhoff facility, survey the fields, plant the perennial crops, buy good foundation livestock, build the processing plants, build the town and buy champagne for the grand opening.

U.S. agriculture, in the hands of the city owners, lenders, speculators and bureaucrats, has been held bondage for several years. This means that the real farmers had to sell their products at wholesale prices and buy at retail. They could not survive in such an adverse commercial climate, and the family farm is dead.

Nucla can survive because it can trade at parity. It can buy anything it needs, money included, with 100 cents to a dollar. It can sell everything for the same kind of money, because America is hungry for good food.

Nucla, further, can be a tourist center, harvesting foreign dollars from people who wish to see its sights. It can schedule tours of ecologically-oriented people and bureaucrats to look at its waste cycling operations, who will spend money, anyway, at Nucla's famous tavern, where we will sell organic wine.

"But," you may ask, "how about it when America's food revolution is over and good foods are everywhere? Then where will your trade advantage be?"

We have been waiting for that question. Nucla, when good foods are everywhere, will be doing just fine. For ten long years its people ate those good foods. They nourished their minds and their souls. They produced America's finest crop of young people, better fed than any youth since 1492. Have no fear. The sinews of Nucla are strong and its mind is free. Its people will always overcome.

By the way, would you like a fresh carrot?